INDEPENDENT LEARNING PROJECT FOR ADVANCED CHEMISTRY

ILPAC
second edition

5

ORGANIC

INTRODUCTION TO ORGANIC CHEMISTRY

REVISED BY ANN LAINCHBURY JOHN STEPHENS ALEC THOMPSON

JOHN MURRAY

■ ACKNOWLEDGEMENTS

We are grateful to CLEAPSS/ASE Laboratory Standards Committee for ensuring that the text meets with current safety recommendations.

Thanks are due to the following examination boards for permission to reproduce questions from past A-level papers: Associated Examining Board: Exercise 59, p. 60 (1979); End-of-unit test 14, p. 110 (1992); 15, p. 111 (1992); 19, p. 111 (1991); 21, p. 112 (1981). Joint Matriculation Board: Exercise 61, p. 65 (1992); Exercise 87, p. 93 (1991); End-of-unit test 1, p. 109 (1992); 16, p. 111 (1991); 17, p. 111 (1991). Oxford and Cambridge Schools Examination Board: Exercise 95, p. 106 (1992); End-of-unit test 23, p. 112 (1992). University of Cambridge Local Examinations Syndicate Teacher-marked exercise, p. 108 (1992); End-of-unit test 22, p. 112 (1991). University of London Examination and Assessments Council: Exercise 38, p. 36 (L 1993); Teacher-marked Exercise, p. 56 (N 1990); Exercise 59, p. 60 (L 1992); Exercise 72, p. 77 (L 1990); Teacher-marked Exercise, p. 86 (N 1991); End-of-unit test 2–5, p. 109 (N 1993); End-of-unit test 6–9, pp. 109–110 (L 1976); End-of-unit test 10–12, p. 110 (L 1981); End-of-unit test 13, p. 110 (N 1993). University of Oxford Delegacy of Local Examinations: End-of-unit test 20, p. 112 (1991). (The examination boards accept no responsibility whatsoever for the accuracy or method of working in the answers given.)

Photographs reproduced by kind permission of AERE Technology (p. 83); Barnaby's Picture Library (p. 55); M. Bond/Science Photo Library (p. 94 top); BP Educational Service (p. 58); British Oxygen (p. 49); J. Burgess/Science Photo Library (p. 80 top); Environmental Picture Library (p. 75, p. 81 top); R. Folwell/ Science Photo Library (p. 57); S. Fraser/Science Photo Library (p. 73); C. Goldin/Science Photo Library (p. 75); Peter Gould (p. 24, p. 25, p. 36); A. Hart-Davies/Science Photo Library (p. 81 bottom); J. Holmes, Hays Chemicals/Science Photo Library (p. 65); NASA/Science Photo Library (p. 76); Royal Society of Chemistry (p. 43). All other photographs by the Last Resort Picture Library. The assistance provided by the staff and students of Roding Valley High School, Loughton, Essex and Tuxford School, Tuxford, Newark, Nottinghamshire for the photographs of the experiments is gratefully acknowledged.

The extract starting on p. 60 is taken from *Nuffield Advanced Science: Chemistry, 3rd Edition, Student's Book*, Longman, 1994, with kind permission from the Nuffield–Chelsea Curriculum Trust. The extract on p. 82 is reproduced with kind permission of *The Guardian*. Figure 7 is taken from *SBS – The Tanker Industry in the 1990s* with kind permission of Shell International Petroleum Company. The data in Figs 11 and 12 and Tables 17 and 18 are reproduced with the kind permission of the Warren Spring Laboratory on behalf of the Department of the Environment (first published in the *Digest of Environmental Protection and Water Statistics* No. 15, 1992, HMSO). Figures 15 and 16 are reproduced with kind permission of BP Educational Service.

The publishers have made every effort to trace the copyright holders, but if they have inadvertently overlooked any, they will be pleased to make the necessary arrangements at the earliest opportunity.

Original material produced by the Independent Learning Project for Advanced Chemistry sponsored by the Inner London Education Authority

First edition published in 1983
by John Murray (Publishers) Ltd
50 Albemarle Street
London W1X 4BD

Second edition 1995
Reprinted 1999

Design and layouts by John Townson/Creation.
Illustrations by Barking Dog Art and Gray Publishing

Produced by Gray Publishing
Typeset in 10/12 pt Times and Helvetica
Printed in Great Britain by St Edmundsbury Press Ltd, Bury St Edmunds

ISBN 0–7195–5335–0

CONTENTS

■ **INTRODUCTION TO ORGANIC CHEMISTRY – HYDROCARBONS**

■ Symbols used in ILPAC

 Computer program

 A-level question

 Discussion

 A-level part question

 Experiment

 A-level question;
Special Paper

 Model-making

 A-level supplementary
question

 Reading

 Revealing Exercise

 Video programme

■ International hazard symbols

 Corrosive

 Oxidising

 Explosive

 Radioactive

 Harmful or irritant

Toxic

 Highly flammable

INTRODUCTION TO
ORGANIC CHEMISTRY

INTRODUCTION

This volume is the first of three on the subject of organic chemistry. You are introduced to organic chemistry in this first volume by studying compounds which consist of carbon and hydrogen only – the hydrocarbons – and compounds which in addition have halogen atoms – the halogen compounds.

We have not separated this volume into parts because there is no obvious progression of difficulty, but the subject matter splits conveniently into seven chapters. After an introduction, we deal with three different families of hydrocarbons – alkanes, alkenes, and arenes. The next chapter covers aspects of the petroleum industry which include the composition of blended petrol and feedstock for the chemicals industry. We then consider air pollution resulting from burning fossil fuels. You will learn about the source of each pollutant, its effect on the environment and health, and some methods to control it. Finally you will study halogen compounds.

There are two experiments in the hydrocarbon section and two in the halogen compound section.

There are two ILPAC video programmes – 'Carbon: The Key to Organic Chemistry' and 'Organic Techniques 1' – designed to accompany this volume. They are not essential, but you should try to see them at the appropriate time if they are available.

■ Pre-knowledge

Before you start work on this volume, you should be able to:

1. Describe the structure of benzene.
2. State how organic compounds generally differ from inorganic compounds in their physical properties.
3. Identify, from formulae, saturated and unsaturated organic compounds.
4. Explain why heavier molecules generally have higher boiling points.
5. Use the electron-pair repulsion theory to suggest shapes for simple molecules.
6. Calculate enthalpy changes of reaction from bond-energy terms.

■ Pre-test

To find out whether you are ready to start this volume, try the following test, which is based on the pre-knowledge items. You should not spend more than 30 minutes on this test. Hand your answers to your teacher for marking.

1. Benzene and cyclohexene react with hydrogen in the presence of a catalyst according to the following equations:

$$C_6H_6 \text{ (l)} + 3H_2 \text{ (g)} \rightarrow C_6H_{12} \text{ (l)}; \quad \Delta H^\ominus = -208 \text{ kJ mol}^{-1}$$
$$C_6H_{10} \text{ (l)} + H_2 \text{ (g)} \rightarrow C_6H_{12} \text{ (l)}; \quad \Delta H^\ominus = -120 \text{ kJ mol}^{-1}$$

The structures of benzene and cyclohexene are often represented as

How do you account for the fact that the enthalpy of hydrogenation of benzene is less than three times that of cyclohexene? (5)

2. Suggest explanations for the following facts.
   a The boiling points of methane, CH_4, ethane, C_2H_6, and propane, C_3H_8, increase in the same order as the molecular masses. (3)
   b Organic compounds are usually more volatile and have lower melting points than inorganic compounds. (2)

3. Classify the following compounds as saturated or unsaturated:

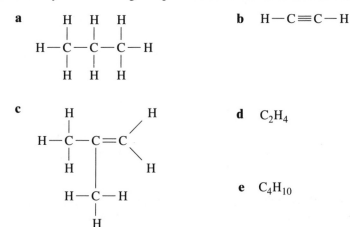

4. This question concerns the following shapes of particles:
   A linear,
   B square planar,
   C trigonal planar,
   D trigonal pyramidal,
   E tetrahedral.
   Which best describes the shape of each of the following ions or molecules?
   a ammonia, NH_3,
   b carbon dioxide, CO_2,
   c methane, CH_4,
   d ammonium ion, NH_4^+,
   e boron trifluoride, BF_3. (5)

(Total: 20 marks)

CHAPTER 1

THE BASIS OF ORGANIC CHEMISTRY

■ 1.1 What is organic chemistry?

Quite simply, organic chemistry is the study of the compounds of carbon. A few simple compounds, especially those containing no hydrogen, are excluded; for example, the oxides and carbonates of carbon are not classed as organic.

The unique properties of carbon, for instance, its ability to form stable chains and rings of atoms, enable it to form millions of organic compounds. We discuss these unique properties further in Volume 11, Group IV Elements.

Your study of organic chemistry has three main aspects.

1. Learning **specific reactions** of organic compounds, and the conditions under which they occur.
2. Studying the **mechanisms** of some of these reactions, i.e. considering why and how they take place.
3. Linking together specific reactions to form **synthetic pathways** by means of which important compounds may be prepared, both in the laboratory and in industry.

At first sight, you might think you have a daunting task ahead. Since there are so many organic compounds of such a wide variety, you might expect a list of their reactions to be almost endless. Fortunately, however, there are two concepts which help us to simplify this information in a systematic way. The first of these concerns **functional groups**, and the second is the idea of a **homologous series**.

■ 1.2 Functional groups

The structure of a typical carbon compound can be considered as two parts: a saturated carbon–hydrogen 'skeleton', which is comparatively unreactive, and a reactive part consisting of one or more functional groups. Two examples are shown in Fig. 1.

Figure 1

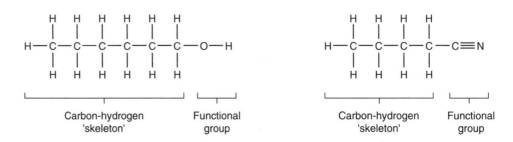

Carbon-hydrogen 'skeleton'	Functional group	Carbon-hydrogen 'skeleton'	Functional group

OBJECTIVE When you have finished this section you should be able to:
■ name, and identify by formulae, ten different functional groups.

If it is available, watch the ILPAC video programme, 'Carbon: The Key to Organic Chemistry'. This will give you a useful introduction to your study of organic chemistry.

Also, read the introductory section to organic chemistry in your textbook, looking for examples of functional groups.

Each functional group has its own distinctive properties. This means that the properties of any organic compound are, to a large extent, the sum of the properties of its functional groups.

We therefore consider a number of functional groups in turn, using specific compounds to illustrate their reactions. When you have learnt these reactions, you will have mastered a sound framework for the whole of organic chemistry.

In Table 1, we list the three simplest functional groups, which contain only carbon–carbon bonds. In the formulae of these groups, the open-ended bond-lines represent attachment to other carbon atoms or to hydrogen atoms. The name of an organic compound usually contains clues that indicate which functional groups are present. We list these name-clues, and also the names of some families of compounds which contain particular groups, together with some examples.

Table 1

Functional group	Family names	Name-clues	Examples
Double bond $\diagdown C = C \diagup$	alkenes	-ene	ethene, $CH_2{=}CH_2$
Triple bond $-C \equiv C-$	alkynes	-yne	ethyne, $CH{\equiv}CH$
Benzene ring	aromatics arenes	-benz-	methylbenzene, $C_6H_5CH_3$
		phen-	phenol, C_6H_5OH

You will study the double bond and benzene functional group in detail in this volume but not the triple bond. However, you will find other functional groups mentioned as products of reactions and in your reading. We therefore list, in Tables 2 and 3, the functional groups you will study in other organic volumes. You need not learn **all** the information in these tables at this stage, especially the names and formulae of the examples, but you will find them useful for reference.

Table 2 lists simple functional groups which contain bonds linking carbon atoms to halogen, oxygen and nitrogen atoms. The functional groups in this table are attached only to carbon atoms, as indicated by the open-ended bond-lines.

Table 2

	Functional group	Family names	Name-clues	Examples
Carbon–halogen bonds	halogeno —F —Cl —Br —I	halogeno-compounds	fluoro- chloro- bromo- iodo-	chloromethane, CH_3Cl iodobutane, C_4H_9I
Carbon–oxygen bonds	hydroxy —O—H or —OH	alcohols	-ol hydroxy-	ethanol, C_2H_5OH hydroxyethanoic acid, CH_2OHCO_2H
	carbonyl $\diagdown$C$=$O or $\diagdown$CO	ketones	-one	propanone, CH_3COCH_3
	$\diagdown$C$=$O or —CHO H	aldehydes	-al	ethanal, CH_3CHO
	ether —O—	ethers	-oxy-	methoxyethane, $CH_3OC_2H_5$
Carbon–nitrogen bonds	amino —N(H)(H) or —NH$_2$	amines (primary)	-amine	ethylamine, $C_2H_5NH_2$ diethylamine, $(C_2H_5)_2NH$ triethylamine, $(C_2H_5)_3N$
	$\diagdown$N–H or $>$NH	(secondary)		
	—N or $>$N	(tertiary)	amino-	aminophenol,
	nitrile —C$\equiv$N or —CN	nitriles	-nitrile	ethanenitrile, C_2H_5CN
	nitro —N($=$O)($\rightarrow$O) or —NO$_2$	nitro compounds	-nitro	nitroethane, $C_2H_5NO_2$

In the first exercise, you identify the functional groups in a number of simple compounds. Do not worry about naming the compounds at this stage – you will learn the naming system step-by-step later on.

EXERCISE 1   Name the functional group(s) in each of the following compounds:

Answers on page 114

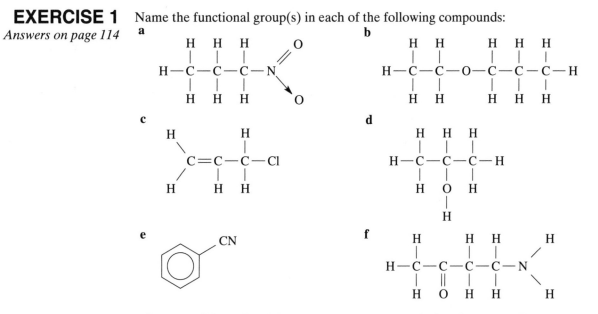

When two of these simple functional groups are attached to the same carbon atom, a multiple functional group may be formed which does **not** have all the properties of the simple groups. In Table 3, we list the five most important of these multiple groups. Generally speaking, they have more similarity to each other than to the simple groups they contain.

Table 3

Functional group	Family names	Name-clues	Examples
Carboxyl $-C\overset{O}{\underset{OH}{}}$ or $-CO_2H$	carboxylic acids	-oic acid	ethanoic acid, CH_3CO_2H
Ester $-C\overset{O}{\underset{O-}{}}$ or $-CO_2-$	esters	-oate	ethyl ethanoate, $CH_3CO_2C_2H_5$
Acyl halide $-C\overset{O}{\underset{Hal}{}}$ or $-COHal$	acyl halides	-oyl halide	ethanoyl chloride, CH_3COCl
Amide $-C\overset{O}{\underset{NH_2}{}}$ or $-CONH_2$	amides	-amide	ethanamide, CH_3CONH_2
Anhydride $-C\overset{O}{\underset{O}{}}$ $-C\underset{O}{}$ or $>(CO)_2O$	anhydrides	-anhydride	ethanoic anhydride, $(CH_3CO)_2O$

In the next exercise you look at some more complex compounds. The names may be familiar to you but you are not expected to memorise the formulae! The point of the exercise is to illustrate the fact that a complex molecule contains simple functional groups, and it is these which help to determine the properties of the substance.

EXERCISE 2

Answers on page 114

Name the functional groups in the following compounds:

a Aspirin

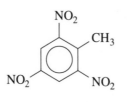

b Paracetamol

c DDT

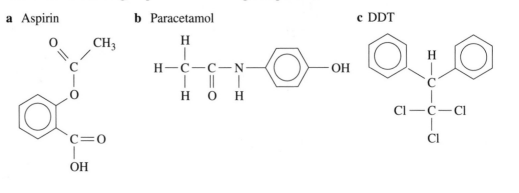

d TNT

e LSD

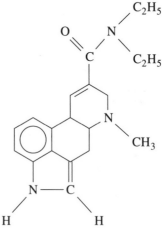

f Pethidine

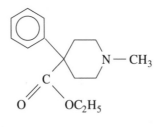

g phenolphthalein

h 2,4,5-T (Herbicide)

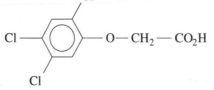

i Dioxin

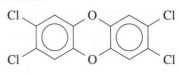

[*continued opposite*]

j Valium

k Monosodium glutamate

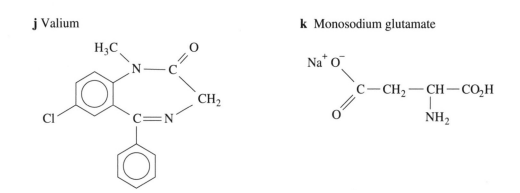

You can see in the last two exercises some of the many possible ways in which atoms can be arranged in organic compounds. To simplify the study of organic chemistry, compounds sharing the same functional group can be grouped together as a class. We can further divide the class into families called homologous series.

■ 1.3 Homologous series

The advantage of considering homologous series of compounds is that the members of a particular series are very much alike chemically.

OBJECTIVES When you have finished this section you should be able to:
■ explain the term **homologous series**;
■ recognise members of the same homologous series by looking at their formulae.

Read about homologous series in your textbook(s). Find out how one member of a series differs in structure from the next so that you can do the next exercise.

EXERCISE 3

Answers on page 114

a What is the difference in structure between one member of a homologous series and the next?
b Which pairs of the following compounds are members of the same homologous series?

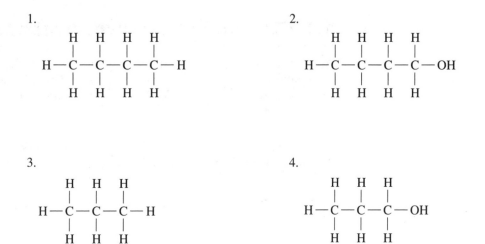

[*continued overleaf*]

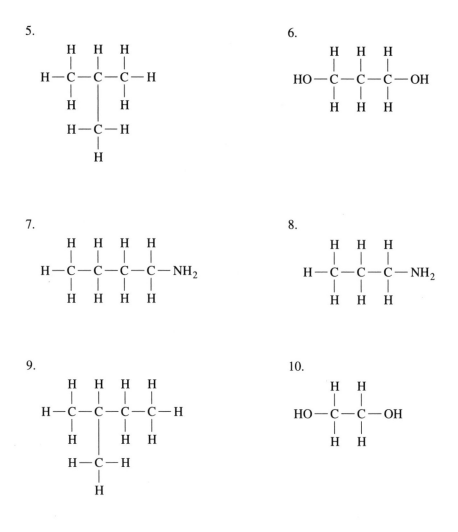

5.

$$H-\overset{\overset{\displaystyle H}{|}}{\underset{\underset{\displaystyle H}{|}}{C}}-\overset{\overset{\displaystyle H}{|}}{C}-\overset{\overset{\displaystyle H}{|}}{\underset{\underset{\displaystyle H}{|}}{C}}-H$$

6.

$$HO-\overset{\overset{\displaystyle H}{|}}{\underset{\underset{\displaystyle H}{|}}{C}}-\overset{\overset{\displaystyle H}{|}}{\underset{\underset{\displaystyle H}{|}}{C}}-\overset{\overset{\displaystyle H}{|}}{\underset{\underset{\displaystyle H}{|}}{C}}-OH$$

7.

8.

9.

10.

Having looked at two of the organising principles of organic chemistry, you now begin your detailed study with the simplest organic compounds, the hydrocarbons.

■ 1.4 Classification of hydrocarbons

As the name suggests, hydrocarbons contain only carbon and hydrogen. You will study three different classes of hydrocarbons in this volume – alkanes, alkenes, and arenes. This classification is based upon the types of carbon–carbon bond in the molecules.

OBJECTIVES When you have finished this section you should be able to:
■ classify **hydrocarbons** by reference to their structural formulae.

Figure 2 shows you how hydrocarbons are classified. Study it and attempt the exercise which follows.

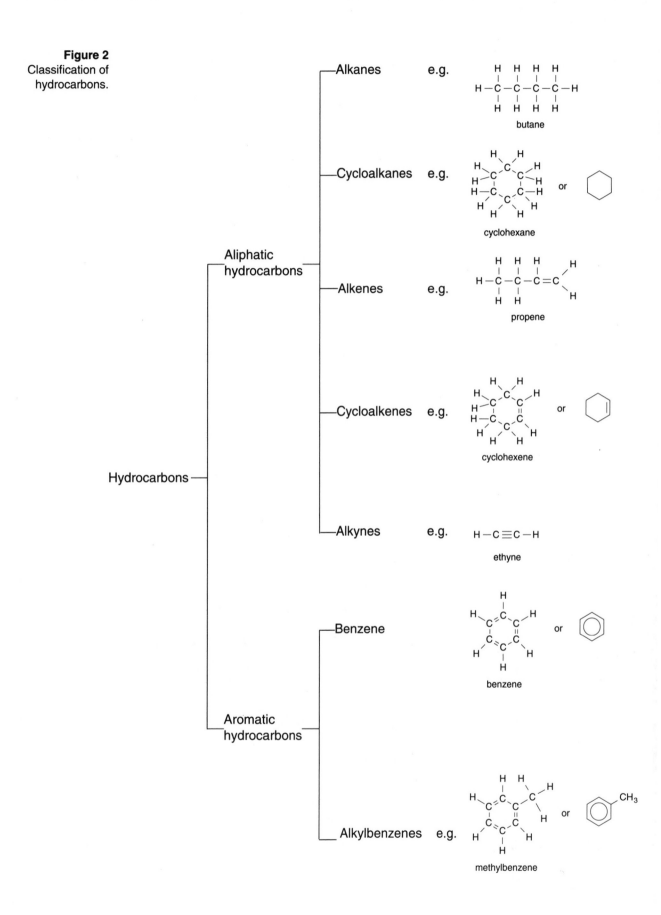

Figure 2
Classification of hydrocarbons.

The words 'aliphatic' and 'aromatic' are not confined to descriptions of hydrocarbons. They simply indicate whether or not compounds contain benzene rings.

'Aliphatic' comes from a Greek word meaning 'fatty'. Aliphatic compounds do form the skeletons of most fats and oils, but the term can be used for many other compounds as well.

'Aromatic' comes from a Greek word meaning 'fragrant-smelling'. This is misleading because many aromatic compounds have a foul smell and may also be toxic.

In the next exercise, you use Fig. 2 (page 11) to classify some hydrocarbons.

EXERCISE 4

Answers on page 114

Classify the following hydrocarbons:

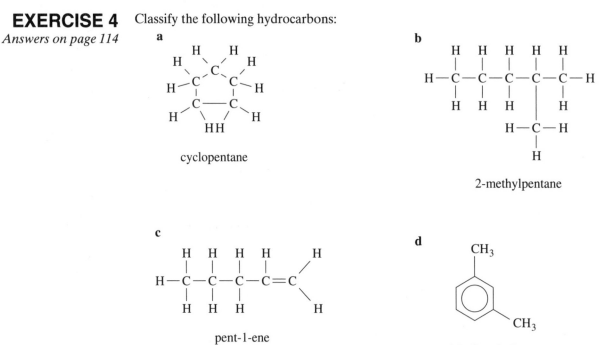

a
cyclopentane

b
2-methylpentane

c
pent-1-ene

d
1,3-dimethylbenzene

We now consider in more detail the simplest class of hydrocarbons, the alkanes.

ALKANES: C—C AND C—H BONDS

The alkanes have been known for a long time and were originally called 'paraffins' (which comes from the Latin meaning 'little affinity', i.e. little reactivity). Their names have 'ane' at the end. They are found in crude oil and natural gas and we use them extensively as fuels and as the starting materials for making a huge variety of organic compounds.

OBJECTIVES

When you have finished the first part of this chapter you should be able to:
- write the general molecular formula of **alkanes**;
- name the first ten members of the **homologous series** of straight-chain alkanes;
- describe the **shapes of alkane molecules**.

Look up the homologous series of straight-chain alkanes in your textbook and learn the names of the first ten members. This is important because they form the basis of the naming of other organic compounds. Look for the **general molecular formula** of this series and note how you can use it to work out the molecular formula of each alkane.

EXERCISE 5

Answers on page 115

a Complete a larger copy of Table 4 for the first seven members of the homologous series of straight-chain alkanes.
b Write the general molecular formula for the alkanes.
c What is the molecular formula of dodecane, which has 12 carbon atoms?

Table 4

	Molecular formula	Structural formula
Methane	CH_4	H | H—C—H | H
Ethane		

You now use models to show the shapes of alkane molecules.

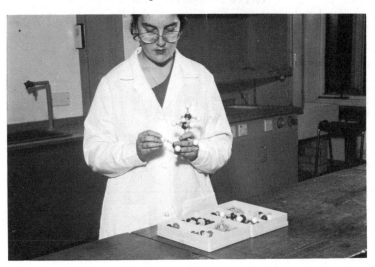

■ 2.1 Shapes of alkane molecules

In ILPAC Volume 3, Bonding and Structure, you made balloon models to describe the shapes of molecules. In this volume we make use of another type of model. The exercise which follows will enable you to describe the shapes of some alkane molecules.

Ask for a model-making kit ('ball-and-spoke' type) and make models of molecules of the first five alkanes shown in Table 4 and of cyclohexane, C_6H_{12}. With the models in front of you, attempt the next exercise. You will need them again for Exercise 8.

EXERCISE 6

Answers on page 116

a Describe the shape of the methane molecule in one word.
b Sketch a methane molecule to show its three-dimensional structure. Mark in values for bond angles.
c Look at your model of pentane. Would you say that the 'straight chain' is really straight?
d Look at your model of ethane. Do you think the positions of the two CH_3 groups are fixed relative to one another, i.e. can you rotate them around the C—C bond?
e When making a model of cyclohexane, you may have noticed that two molecular shapes are possible. One is known as the 'chair' form and the other the 'boat' form. Draw the shape of each – their names should give a clue.

When the tetrahedral shape of the methane molecule is relevant to our discussion, we can represent it on paper by using ordinary lines for bonds in the plane of the paper, dashed lines for bonds directed behind the paper, and tapered lines for bonds directed in front of the paper. (See below left.) More often, the two-dimensional representation (below right) is adequate.

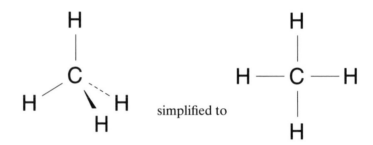

You will have seen that molecules such as propane, C_3H_8, and pentane, C_5H_{12}, should really be represented as zig-zag chains, with each carbon atom having tetrahedrally directed bonds (Fig. 3).

Figure 3

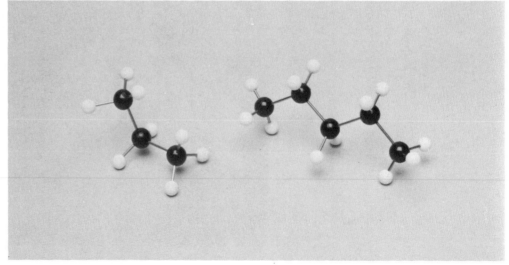

Again, for simplicity, we often represent them on paper as straight chains.

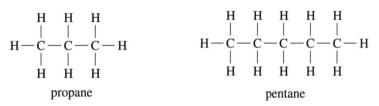

propane   pentane

These full structural formulae ('displayed formula') can take up considerable space on paper so, for simplicity, we often write condensed structural formulae, as shown:

$CH_3CH_2CH_3$ $CH_3CH_2CH_2CH_2CH_3$
propane   pentane

The structural formula of pentane can be condensed even further to $CH_3(CH_2)_3CH_3$.
    To check that you understand the different ways of writing formulae, try the next exercise.

EXERCISE 7   Write the formula of hexane (straight chain) in four different ways.
Answer on page 116

When you were making your models of the molecules of butane, C_4H_{10}, and pentane, C_5H_{12}, you might have seen that it is possible to attach the same atoms in different ways to give branched carbon chains rather than straight ones. Different structures which have the same molecular formulae are called isomers.

■ 2.2 Structural isomerism in alkanes

OBJECTIVES   When you have finished this section you should be able to:
■ give examples of **structural isomerism** in alkanes;
■ write the structural formulae and names of **branched-chain** alkanes.

 The best way to find out whether an alkane has any isomers is by making models and trying to rearrange the same atoms into different structures. Use a model-making kit to help you with the following exercises.

EXERCISE 8   How many different structures are represented below?
Answers on page 116

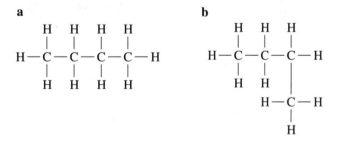

[*continued overleaf*]

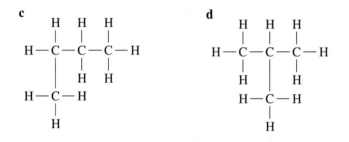

EXERCISE 9

Answers on page 117

a Complete a larger copy of Table 5 in your notes by drawing all the possible structures for each alkane.

b Which compounds have no isomers?

Table 5

Molecular formula	Structural formula of straight chain	Were any other arrangements possible? If yes, draw their structural formulae
CH_4		Yes/No
C_2H_6		Yes/No
C_3H_8		Yes/No
C_4H_{10}		Yes/No
C_5H_{12}		Yes/No
C_6H_{14}		Yes/No

You will see from the last exercise how the number of isomers increases rapidly with the addition of CH_2 groups to the molecular formula. In fact, there are as many as 4.11×10^9 isomers of molecular formula $C_{30}H_{62}$!

The type of isomerism you have just studied is one example of structural isomerism known as 'chain isomerism'. In general, structural isomerism occurs where compounds have the same molecular formula but different structural formulae, i.e. to change one structural isomer to another, bonds have to be broken and remade at different sites. You will meet other types of isomerism later in your course.

Now that you understand the term 'isomerism', you learn how to name and write the structural formulae of some isomers.

■ 2.3 Writing structural formulae and naming alkanes

We give you Worked Examples to show you how to draw structural formulae of alkanes from the names, and vice versa. You will build on this system of naming as you study more and more compounds, but first here are some things you must learn.

1. The number of carbon atoms in a chain is shown by basing the names of compounds on the following 'stems'.

Number of carbon atoms	1	2	3	4	5	6	7	8	9	10
Stem	meth	eth	prop	but	pent	hex	hept	oct	non	dec

2. The 'ane' at the end of the name of a hydrocarbon means it is an alkane, e.g. propane

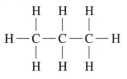

3. Branches are called 'meth**yl**', 'eth**yl**', 'prop**yl**', etc., depending on the number of carbon atoms they contain.

You must be able to write the structural formula from the name of a compound. We show you how this is done in the following Worked Example.

WORKED EXAMPLE   Draw the structural formula of the alkane 3-ethyl-2,5-dimethylheptane.

Solution   1. Identify the longest carbon chain by looking at the stem or stems.
-**hept**ane – 7 carbon atoms
2. Write down the carbon atoms in the longest chain and number them. (This is usually done from right to left.)

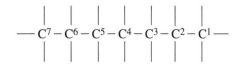

3. Add the carbon atoms of the branches in the correct positions. 3-Ethyl means 'an ethyl group, C_2H_5, attached to C^3' and 2,5-**di**methyl means '**two** methyl groups, CH_3, attached to C^2 and C^5'.

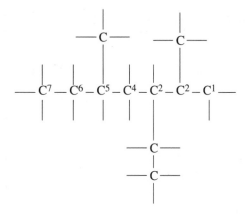

4. 'Fill in' with hydrogen atoms so that each carbon atom makes four bonds.

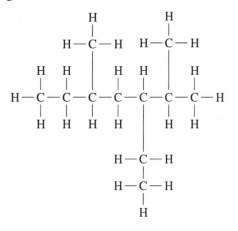

(We have elongated three C—C bonds simply for convenience, to avoid overcrowding the diagram. Of course, they are not elongated in the molecule, as you can see from your models.)

Now attempt the following exercise.

EXERCISE 10

Answers on page 118

Draw the structural formulae of the compounds below.
a 2,2-dimethylbutane,
b 3-ethyl-2,4-dimethylpentane,
c 2,3,4-trimethylhexane,
d 3-ethyl-2-methylheptane.

You must also be able to write the name from the structural formula of a compound, i.e. the reverse of the above procedure. We show you how this is done in Worked Examples.

WORKED EXAMPLE

Name the alkane

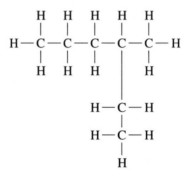

Solution

1. Find the longest unbranched chain and write down the name of the corresponding alkane. (Beware! The chain may not be drawn 'straight'.)

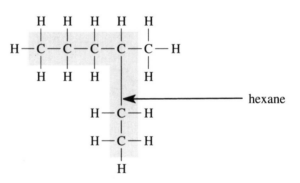

hexane

2. Number the carbon chain from the end nearest the branch.

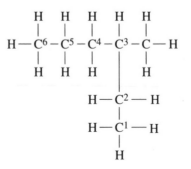

3. Write down in front of the carbon-chain name:
   i)   chain position,
   ii) dash -,
   iii) name of the branch.

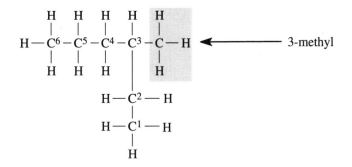
3-methyl

Full name: **3-methylhexane**.

Now try some exercises for yourself.

EXERCISE 11   Name the following compounds.
Answers on page 118

a
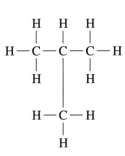

b
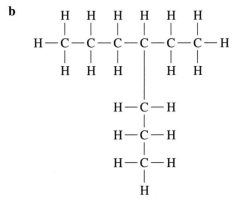

c
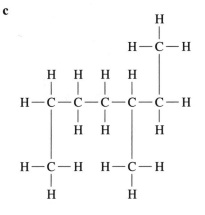

We now give you another Worked Example, this time to show you how to name an alkane with more than one branch.

WORKED EXAMPLE   Name the compound

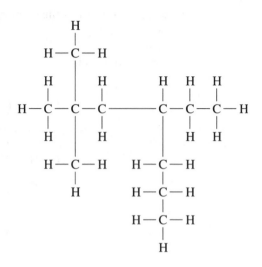

Solution   1. Find the longest chain and write down its name.

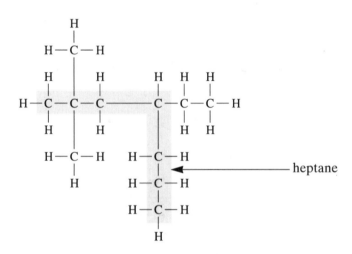

heptane

2. Number the carbon chain from the end nearest the most branches. If you are not sure which end this is, it is the one which gives the lowest total of numbers in the final name.

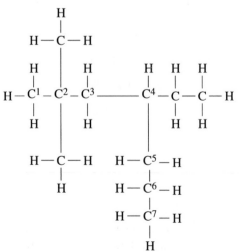

3. Write down in front of the carbon-chain name, all the names of the branches in alphabetical order with their chain position numbers. If there are more than one of the same branch, use 'di', 'tri', etc.

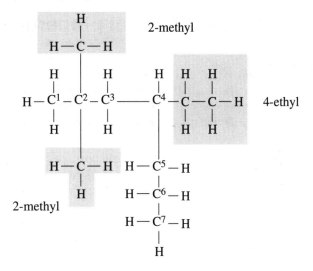

Full name: **4-ethyl-2,2-dimethylheptane**. (Numbering from the other end would give 4-ethyl-6,6-dimethylheptane, which does not contain the lowest total of numbers.)

Now you can try the procedure yourself in the next exercise.

EXERCISE 12

Answers on page 118

Name the following alkanes:

a

b

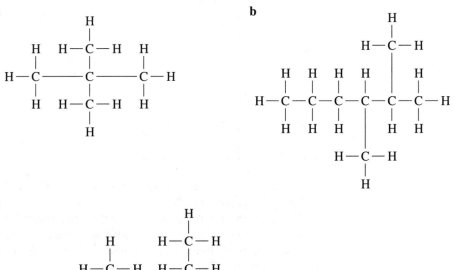

c

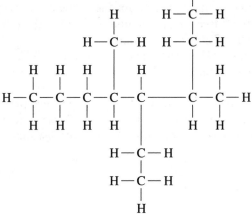

We now consider how variations in structure affect the physical properties of the alkanes.

■ 2.4 Physical properties of alkanes

OBJECTIVES

When you have finished this section you should be able to:
■ relate the trends in **physical properties** of a homologous series to structure;
■ describe the effect on physical properties of **branching** in non-linear alkanes;
■ list the general characteristics of a **homologous series**.

Read about the general characteristics of a homologous series. In particular, look for an account of the trends in physical properties in the 'straight-chain' alkanes, and the way in which branching affects physical properties. You should then be able to do the following exercises.

EXERCISE 13

Answers on page 118

Using your data book, complete Table 6 and answer the questions which follow.

Table 6

Formula	Name	Boiling point/K	Melting point/K	Density/g cm^{-3}
CH_4	methane			
C_2H_6	ethane			
C_3H_8	propane			
C_4H_{10}	butane			
C_5H_{12}	pentane			
C_6H_{14}	hexane			
C_7H_{16}	heptane			
C_8H_{18}	octane			
C_9H_{20}	nonane			
$C_{10}H_{22}$	decane			

a What trends are shown in the physical properties of the homologous series of straight-chain alkanes?
b Plot a graph of boiling point (*y*-axis) against the number of carbon atoms for the alkanes and explain the reason for the shape of the graph.
c Use your graph to estimate the boiling point of dodecane, $C_{12}H_{26}$.
d Use the data in Table 6 to estimate
   i) the formula of the first alkane to be solid at 20°C,
   ii) the density of tetradecane, $C_{14}H_{30}$.

In Exercise 13 you saw the steady change in physical properties on descending the homologous series of straight-chain alkanes. This is one of the general characteristics of any homologous series; in the next exercise you list some more.

EXERCISE 14

Answers on page 120

Which of the following statements are general characteristics of a homologous series?

a All the compounds can be represented by a single general molecular formula.
b All the compounds have the same structural formula.
c The structure of each member differs from the next by a $-CH_2-$ group.
d The physical properties of adjacent members are similar.
e The physical properties show a steady change with increasing molar mass.
f Adjacent members become more and more alike with increasing molar mass.

In the next exercise, you look at the effect of chain-branching on boiling point. You will find it helpful to construct 'space-filling' models, i.e. models in which atoms are in close contact. Ask your teacher.

EXERCISE 15

Answers on page 120

Look at the information in Table 7 and explain the observed trend in boiling points. If possible, construct space-filling models of each of the isomers of pentane.

Table 7

Name and molecular formula	Structural formula	Boiling point/K
Pentane, C_5H_{12}	$CH_3-CH_2-CH_2-CH_2-CH_3$	309
2-Methylbutane, C_5H_{12}	$CH_3-CH-CH_2-CH_3$ $\quad\quad\;\; \mid$ $\quad\quad\; CH_3$	301
2,2-Dimethylpropane, C_5H_{12}	$\quad\quad\;\; CH_3$ $\quad\quad\;\; \mid$ CH_3-C-CH_3 $\quad\quad\;\; \mid$ $\quad\quad\;\; CH_3$	283

Another characteristic of a homologous series is that each member can be expected to show similar chemical reactions. You need only study the chemical properties of one member of the series in order to predict those of the others.

■ 2.5 Chemical properties of alkanes

OBJECTIVES When you have finished this section you should be able to:
■ write equations for the **reactions of alkanes**, stating the necessary conditions;
■ explain, in general terms, what takes place in a **substitution reaction**.

In Exercise 16 we ask you to make a prediction about the reactivity of alkanes. After that you do an experiment to test your prediction.

EXERCISE 16
Answers on page 120

a Look up the C—C and C—H bond energies in your data book. Are these values higher or lower than most of the other single bonds listed?
b What does your answer to part **a** suggest about the reactivity of alkanes?

In the next experiment you test the reactivity of the alkanes by carrying out a few simple test-tube reactions.

Before starting the experiment, you should have a class discussion with your teacher on the hazards of using organic chemicals in the laboratory.

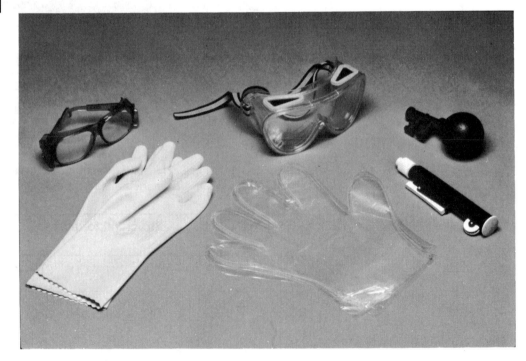

EXPERIMENT 1   Chemical properties of alkanes

Aim The purpose of this experiment is to test the reactivity of the alkanes using cyclohexane as an example.

Introduction We have chosen cyclohexane as an example of an alkane because it is a liquid, which makes it easy to handle, and because it is cheap. It has virtually the same reactions as hexane and is very similar to other alkanes. It is also less hazardous to use than hexane. You use cyclohexane in five simple test-tube reactions.

Requirements
- safety spectacles
- protective gloves
- cyclohexane (with teat pipette)
- hard glass watch glass
- Bunsen burner and bench protection mat
- wood splints
- beaker, 250 cm^3
- 1 dry test-tube covered in aluminium foil
- 5 dry test-tubes with corks to fit
- test-tube rack
- bromine dissolved in an inert solvent
- lamp with 100 watt bulb
- ammonia solution, 5 M NH_3
- dilute sulphuric acid, 1 M H_2SO_4
- potassium manganate(VII) solution, 0.01 M $KMnO_4$
- concentrated sulphuric acid, H_2SO_4

HAZARD WARNING Bromine is dangerously toxic and corrosive, especially in its liquid state. Solutions, such as those used in this experiment, must also be treated with care. Therefore you **must**:
■ Do the experiment in a fume cupboard.
■ Keep the top on the bottle as much as possible.
■ Wear gloves and safety spectacles.
Cyclohexane is very flammable. Therefore you **must**:
■ Keep the top on the bottle as much as possible.
■ Keep the bottle away from flames.
■ Wear safety spectacles.
Ammonia solution (5 M) is an irritant. Take great care when opening bottles on a hot day. You **must**:
■ Wear safety spectacles.
Concentrated sulphuric acid is very corrosive and reacts violently with water. Therefore you **must**:
■ Wear gloves and safety spectacles.
■ Dispose of unwanted acid by **cooling** and pouring **slowly** into an excess of water.

Procedure

A. **Combustion**
   1. Place your watch glass on a bench protection sheet in the fume cupboard. Put on safety spectacles and make sure the extractor in the fume cupboard is switched on.
   2. Using a teat pipette, place 3–4 drops of cyclohexane on the watch glass.
   3. Stopper and remove the bottle of cyclohexane to a safe place away from the watch glass and any Bunsen flames.
   4. Pull down the front of the fume cupboard leaving a 30 cm opening.
   5. Light a long splint and use this to light the cyclohexane. Lower the front of the fume cupboard to a 10 cm opening.
   6. Write down, in a larger copy of Results Table 1:
      a the colour of the flame,
      b whether you can see any soot produced.

B. **Reaction of bromine (dissolved in inert solvent)**
      Put on safety spectacles and make sure the extractor in the fume cupboard is switched on.
   1. Place the test-tube covered with aluminium foil in a rack in the fume cupboard. Put an uncovered tube alongside. Put on safety spectacles and gloves.
   2. Using a teat pipette, place approximately 2 cm^3 of cyclohexane in each test-tube.
   3. Stopper the cyclohexane and remove it to a safe place away from flames.
   4. Pull down the front of the fume cupboard leaving a 30 cm opening.
   5. Using a teat pipette, place in each tube five drops of a solution of bromine in inert solvent.
   6. Stopper the bromine bottle.
   7. Shine the lamp on both test-tubes for about 3 minutes.
   8. A gas is given off during this experiment. Think what gas could be given off and work out a test for the gas. Note the test and its result in your Results Table.
   9. Note the appearance of the contents of the clear test-tube.
   10. Pour the contents of the test-tube covered with aluminium foil into a clean test-tube. Note its appearance.

C. **Reaction of acidified potassium manganate(VII)**
   1. Place a test-tube in a rack in the fume cupboard.
   2. Using a test pipette, place 3–4 drops of cyclohexane in the test-tube.
   3. Stopper and remove the bottle of cyclohexane to a safe place, away from flames.
   4. Pour into the test-tube approximately 1 cm^3 of dilute sulphuric acid and gently agitate the mixture.

5. Pour into the test-tube 5–6 drops of potassium manganate(VII) solution and shake the mixture.
6. Note the appearance of the reaction mixture.

D. **Reaction of concentrated sulphuric acid**

1. Place a test-tube in a rack in the fume cupboard.
2. Pour into the test-tube approximately 1 cm^3 of concentrated sulphuric acid.
3. Pour into the test-tube approximately 1 cm^3 of cyclohexane.
4. Stopper and remove the bottle of cyclohexane to a safe place, away from flames.
5. Note whether the substances mix or form two separate layers.
6. Dispose of this solution by adding it to a beaker of water.

Results Table 1

Reactions of alkanes

Reaction	Observations
A. **Combustion**	
Appearance of flame	
Sootiness	
B. **Action of bromine** (in inert solvent)	
1. In dark	
2. In light	
Identification of gas	
C. **Action of acidified potassium manganate(VII)**	
D. **Action of concentrated sulphuric acid**	

(Specimen results on page 120.)

Questions

Answers on page 120

1. Was your prediction made in Exercise 16 verified by experiment?
2. **a** What are the products of complete combustion of the alkanes?
   b Use your data book to write full thermochemical equations for the combustion of methane, ethane and propane.
   c How do your answers to part **b** relate to the uses of the alkanes?
3. **a** What is meant by the term 'substitution reaction'? Refer to your organic textbook(s).
   b Complete the following equation for the substitution reaction between equal amounts of cyclohexane and bromine.

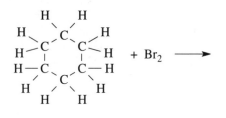

   c What conditions favour the reaction shown in **b** above?
   d In the presence of excess bromine, it is possible to substitute more than one hydrogen atom per molecule of alkane. Write four equations showing all the possible substitution products of reaction between bromine and methane, CH$_4$, in sunlight. Name the products.

Substitution reactions of alkanes are important as the first stages in preparing a wide variety of organic compounds, as you will see in ILPAC Volume 8, Functional Groups.

In the next two sections, you learn the steps by which a typical substitution reaction proceeds, i.e. the reaction mechanism.

■ 2.6 Organic reaction mechanisms

First, you must become familiar with some of the terms used in the study of reaction mechanisms.

OBJECTIVES When you have finished this section you should be able to:
- describe the difference between **homolytic fission** and **heterolytic fission**;
- define the terms **carbocation** (carbonium ion), **carbanion**, and **free radical**;
- distinguish between **electrophiles (electrophilic reagents)** and **nucleophiles (nucleophilic reagents)**.

 Look up the meanings of the terms mentioned in the objectives above. This will enable you to do the following exercises. If these terms are not shown in the index of your textbook, look for them in the chapter or section under the heading **free radical reaction** or **chain reaction**.

EXERCISE 17

Answers on page 121

Copy the following statements and complete them by inserting one of the following words:

homolytic, **free radical**, **heterolytic**, **carbocation**, **carbanion**, **positive**, **negative**, **reactive**, **electrophilic**, **nucleophilic**.

a i) In . . . . . . fission a bond splits so that one bonding electron is attached to each atom,

e.g. $Br \overset{\bullet}{\underset{\bullet}{-}} Br \rightarrow Br\bullet + \bullet Br$

ii) The product of this type of fission has an unpaired electron and is called a . . . . . .

b i) In . . . . . . fission a bond splits so that one atom takes both electrons, e.g.

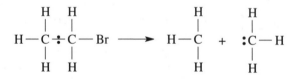

ii) In the example above, the organic radical without the bonding electron will carry a . . . . . . charge and is called a . . . . . .

iii) The organic radical which has taken both electrons from the bond will carry a . . . . . . charge and is called a . . . . . .

c Particles that are attracted to positive charges are called . . . . . . whilst particles that are attracted to negative charges are called . . . . . .

EXERCISE 18

Answers on page 121

a Draw and label the three possible ways the hydrogen–chlorine bond in HCl could split.

b Use data from electronegativity tables to decide which type of fission you think the most likely.

EXERCISE 19

Answers on page 121

Identify the following species as free radicals, carbocations or carbanions. (Charges are not shown.)

a CH₃•

b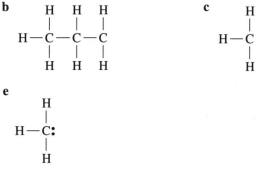

c

d C₂H₅•

e

EXERCISE 20

Answers on page 121

Here is a mixed-up list of nucleophiles and electrophiles. Sort them out and write them down in two columns headed Nucleophiles and Electrophiles.

Br⁻, ROH, RO⁻, I⁺, NO₂⁺, Cl⁻, CN⁻
H⁺, H⁻, RCO₂⁻, NH₃, OH⁻, H₂O, I⁻, Cl⁺.

As you are now familiar with some of the terms used in the study of reaction mechanisms, we can turn our attention to the detailed study of the mechanism for substitution of alkanes.

■ 2.7 Mechanism for substitution in alkanes

In Experiment 1, you saw how cyclohexane and bromine react together in the presence of ultraviolet light. A similar reaction occurs between methane and chlorine and, as this particular reaction has been well researched, we use it in our discussion.

OBJECTIVE   When you have finished this section you should be able to:
■ describe the mechanism for the reaction between chlorine and methane.

Read about the mechanism for the chlorination of methane in your textbook(s) and then attempt the Revealing Exercise which follows.

EXERCISE

Revealing

The overall equation for the reaction between equal amounts of methane and chlorine is:

$$CH_4 \text{ (g)} + Cl_2 \text{ (g)} \rightarrow CH_3Cl \text{ (g)} + HCl \text{ (g)}$$

In this exercise, you see how the mechanism for the reaction can be deduced from five pieces of evidence listed as follows (A to E).

A. The rate of halogenation of an alkane is greater in light.

B. In order to have any effect on this reaction, the light must have a wavelength of not more than 400 nm, which is equivalent to an energy of at least 300 kJ mol⁻¹ (i.e. per mole of photons).

C. In suitable light, chlorination of methane occurs rapidly at room temperature and for each photon of light absorbed, many thousands of molecules of chloromethane are formed.

D. No molecular hydrogen is detected during the course of this reaction but a trace of ethane is produced.

E. Standard enthalpy changes (in kJ mol^{-1}) for some gas-phase reactions:

$CH_4 \rightarrow CH_3\bullet + H\bullet$	+	435
$Cl_2 \rightarrow 2Cl\bullet$	+	242
$CH_3Cl \rightarrow CH_3\bullet + Cl\bullet$	+	350
$HCl \rightarrow H\bullet + Cl\bullet$	+	431
$Cl\bullet + e^- \rightarrow Cl^-$	–	355
$Cl\bullet \rightarrow Cl^+ + e^-$	+	1260
$CH_3\bullet \rightarrow CH_3^+ + e^-$	+	949
$H\bullet \rightarrow H^+ + e^-$	+	1310
$H\bullet + e^- \rightarrow H^-$	–	78
$CH_3\bullet + e^- \rightarrow CH_3^-$	+	2500

Note the use of a • to indicate the unpaired electron in a free radical.

Q1 Which piece of evidence suggests that the chlorination of methane is a chain reaction, i.e. a self-sustaining reaction consisting of a series of steps initiated by the one before?

A1 Evidence C.

Q2 Use evidence B and E, and Hess' law, to decide which of the following reactions could be the first step in the chlorination of methane.

$$CH_4 \rightarrow CH_3\bullet + H\bullet$$
$$CH_4 \rightarrow CH_3^+ + H^-$$
$$Cl_2 \rightarrow 2Cl\bullet$$
$$Cl_2 \rightarrow Cl^+ + Cl^-$$

A2 $\qquad\qquad Cl_2 \rightarrow 2Cl\bullet; \quad \Delta H^{\oplus} = +242 \text{ kJ mol}^{-1}$ $\qquad$ (reaction 1)

The absorption of light of wavelength below 400 nm could provide sufficient energy for this reaction to occur, but the others require far more energy.

$$Cl_2 \rightarrow Cl^+ + Cl^-; \quad \Delta H^{\oplus} = (+242 - 355 + 1260) = +1147 \text{ kJ mol}^{-1}$$

$$CH_4 \rightarrow CH_3\bullet + H\bullet; \quad \Delta H^{\oplus} = +435 \text{ kJ mol}^{-1}$$

$$CH_4 \rightarrow CH_3^+ + H^-; \quad \Delta H^{\oplus} = (+435 + 949 - 78) = +1306 \text{ kJ mol}^{-1}$$

Q3 Suggest two reactions in which the chlorine atoms produced in reaction (1) could go on to react with methane molecules.

A3 $\qquad\qquad Cl\bullet + CH_4 \rightarrow CH_3Cl + H\bullet$

$\qquad\qquad Cl\bullet + CH_4 \rightarrow CH_3\bullet + HCl$

Q4 Use the enthalpy data in evidence E, and evidence D, to predict which of the reactions in **A3** is more likely to occur. (You will need to apply Hess' law in order to determine the enthalpy change for each reaction.)

A4 $$Cl\bullet + CH_4 \rightarrow CH_3\bullet + HCl \qquad \text{(reaction 2)}$$

For this reaction, $\Delta H^\circ = (+435 - 431) = +4 \text{ kJ mol}^{-1}$
but for

$$Cl\bullet + CH_4 \rightarrow CH_3Cl + H\bullet; \quad \Delta H^\circ = (+435 - 350) = +85 \text{ kJ mol}^{-1}$$

It is likely that the less endothermic reaction will occur the more readily. Also, if the first reaction in **A3** were to occur, some molecular hydrogen would be produced by combination of H• free radicals.

Q5 Suggest the next step. (Clue: since this is a chain reaction, another chlorine free radical must be regenerated.)

A5 $$CH_3\bullet + Cl_2 \rightarrow CH_3Cl + Cl\bullet \qquad \text{(reaction 3)}$$

Q6 Steps (2) and (3) can now be repeated indefinitely unless the free radicals are removed in some other way.

Suggest reactions involving the products of the previous steps, (1), (2) and (3), which would terminate the chain reaction, by removing the reactive radicals.

A6 $$2CH_3\bullet \rightarrow C_2H_6 \qquad \text{(reaction 4)}$$
$$2Cl\bullet \rightarrow Cl_2 \qquad \text{(reaction 5)}$$
$$CH_3\bullet + Cl\bullet \rightarrow CH_3Cl \qquad \text{(reaction 6)}$$

This type of reaction is called free radical substitution. The following exercise illustrates further evidence for the proposed mechanism of this reaction.

EXERCISE 21
Answer on page 121

It is found that the rate of the reaction

$$CH_4 + Cl_2 \rightarrow CH_3Cl + HCl$$

is increased by carrying out the reaction in the dark in the presence of tetramethyl lead(IV), which is known to decompose according to the following equation:

$$Pb(CH_3)_4 \rightarrow Pb + 4CH_3\bullet$$

How does this evidence support the mechanism proposed in the Revealing Exercise above?

You should go through the Revealing Exercise several times until you understand the steps involved in the mechanism for the chlorination of methane. You can then test yourself by attempting Exercise 22.

EXERCISE 22

Answers on page 122

a Complete a larger copy of Table 8, making very brief notes on each step of the mechanism for the chlorination of methane.

Table 8

Mechanism for chlorination of methane

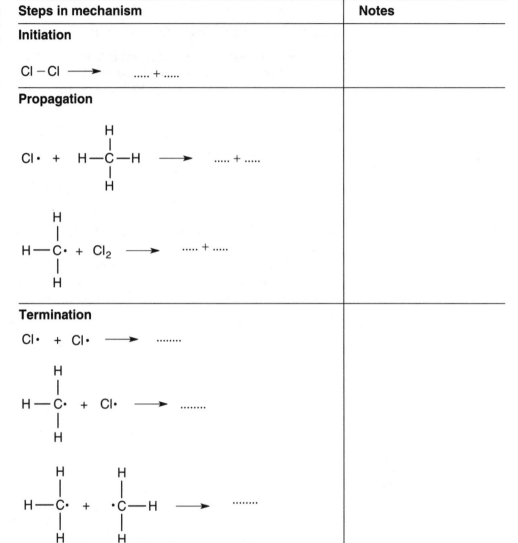

Steps in mechanism	Notes
Initiation	
Cl – Cl ⟶ ..... + ...	
Propagation	
Cl· + H—C—H ⟶ ..... + ...	
H—C· + Cl₂ ⟶ ..... + ...	
Termination	
Cl· + Cl· ⟶	
H—C· + Cl· ⟶	
H—C· + ·C—H ⟶	

b You know that if excess chlorine is present, further substitution can occur to give CH_2Cl_2, $CHCl_3$ and CCl_4. Suggest a mechanism.

c Why is there hardly any reaction between chlorine and methane in the dark?

The combustion of alkanes, and their substitution reactions with halogens, are very important reactions in industry. Nevertheless, you can regard the alkanes as unreactive because they are unaffected by nearly all reagents in usual laboratory conditions. This means that you can now focus your attention on the chemistry of functional groups. In your study, the first class of compounds with a functional group is the alkenes.

ALKENES: C=C BOND

Alkenes are unsaturated compounds which contain one or more C=C bonds.

OBJECTIVES

When you have finished the first part of this chapter you should be able to:
- write the **general molecular formula** of alkenes;
- name **alkenes**;
- describe the **shapes** of alkene molecules;
- describe **geometrical isomerism** in alkenes.

Read the introductory section on alkenes in your textbook(s). Look for the general molecular formula and names of the homologous series of straight-chain alkenes. Refresh your memory of the structure of ethene from ILPAC Volume 3, Bonding and Structure.

EXERCISE 23

Answers on page 123

a Complete a larger copy of Table 9 for the first five members of the homologous series of straight-chain alkenes.

Table 9

Name	Molecular formula	Structural formula
Ethene	C_2H_4	$\begin{array}{c} H \qquad\qquad H \\ \diagdown\qquad\diagup \\ C{=}C \\ \diagup\qquad\diagdown \\ H \qquad\qquad H \end{array}$

b Write the general molecular formula for the alkenes.

c Why is it necessary to include the number '1' in the names from but-1-ene onwards?

In the homologous series of alkenes shown in Table 9, the '1' in the name is the chain position number of the double bond carbon atom nearest the end of the chain. It is, of course, possible for the double bond to be positioned at different sites along the chains and there are certain rules you must follow in naming these particular alkenes.

■ 3.1 Naming alkenes

The rules for naming the alkenes are similar to those for alkanes except that the names end with **-ene** instead of **-ane** and a number is included to show the position of the double bond.

To locate the double bond, you number the carbon atoms in the chain from the end nearest the double bond and then use the **lower** of the two numbers at the ends of the double bond, e.g.

$$\begin{array}{c} \quad\; H \quad\; H \quad\; H \quad\; H \quad\; H \quad\; H \\ \quad\; | \quad\;\; | \quad\;\; | \quad\;\; | \quad\;\; | \quad\;\; | \\ H-C^1-C^2{=}C^3-C^4-C^5-C^6-H \qquad \text{hex-2-ene (not hex-3-ene)} \\ \quad\; | \qquad\qquad | \quad\; | \quad\; | \\ \quad\; H \qquad\qquad\; H \quad\, H \quad\, H \end{array}$$

Where there is chain-branching, the chain on which the name is based must contain the double bond, even though it may not necessarily be the longest chain in the molecule. Also the numbering is chosen so that the carbon atoms carrying the double bonds bear the smallest numbers possible, e.g.

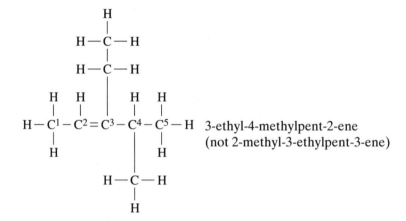

3-ethyl-4-methylpent-2-ene (not 2-methyl-3-ethylpent-3-ene)

If there is more than one double bond, add 'a' to the stem name; use the lower numbers and 'di', 'tri', etc., e.g.

$$H - \overset{\underset{|}{H}}{\underset{\underset{|}{H}}{C^6}} - \overset{\underset{|}{H}}{C^5} = \overset{\underset{|}{H}}{C^4} - \overset{\underset{|}{H}}{\underset{\underset{|}{H}}{C^3}} - \overset{\underset{|}{H}}{C^2} = \overset{\underset{|}{H}}{C^1}$$

hexa-1,4-diene (not hexa-2,5-diene)

You should always try to write the correct name, but you can take some comfort from the fact that examination boards may accept an incorrect name provided that it clearly and unambiguously describes the structural formula. In the second and third examples above, either name might be acceptable. The alternative in the first example is **not** acceptable because it represents a different structure, as you see in the next exercise.

EXERCISE 24

Answers on page 123

a Give the names of:
  i) $CH_3CH_2CH_2CH_2CH=CH_2$,
  ii) $CH_3CH=C=CH_2$,
  iii) $CH_3CH=CHCH_3$,
  iv) $(CH_3)_2C=CHCH_3$.
b Give the structural formulae for:
  i) hex-3-ene,
  ii) 3-methylhex-1-ene,
  iii) 2,5-dimethylhex-2-ene.

You now use models to illustrate the shapes of alkenes

■ 3.2 Shapes of alkene molecules

In ILPAC Volume 3, Bonding and Structure, we considered a rather complex representation of an ethene molecule and you learned that the double bond is considered to be made up of a σ-bond and a π-bond. However, in the next activity, you will use the simpler 'bent-bond' idea to construct a simple ball-and-spring model of ethene. This is an adequate model for many purposes.

Collect a model-making kit and make a model of a molecule of ethene, C_2H_4. You should use four-hole carbon atoms and long, flexible bonds. With the model in front of you, attempt the next exercise.

EXERCISE 25

Answers on page 124

a Describe, in one word, the shape of the ethene molecule.
b Sketch the structure of the ethene molecule and mark in the bond angles (approximate).
c Does the model suggest free rotation about the C=C bonds in ethene?

From your model of ethene, it will be obvious that a double bond makes a molecule more rigid than a singly bonded molecule. Single bonds allow rotation, double bonds do not. It is this property of double bonds which gives rise to another type of isomerism called geometrical isomerism.

■ 3.3 Geometrical isomerism in alkenes

Make models of the following structures for but-2-ene, C_4H_8, and attempt the exercise which follows. You should make the double bond first before positioning the other atoms.

EXERCISE 26

Answer on page 124

Is it possible to change one of the structures **a** or **b** above into the other without breaking any bonds? Explain.

The two structures you have made for but-2-ene are different even though the CH_3 groups are bonded to the same carbon atom in both compounds – it is their arrangement in space that is different. This is an example of geometrical isomerism.

We need names to distinguish between the two isomers of but-2-ene. We do this by adding the prefixes '*cis*' and '*trans*'.

cis-but-2-ene
(substituent groups
on one side of
the double bond)

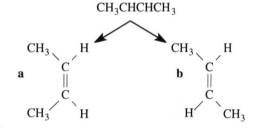

trans-but-2-ene
(substituent groups
on different sides
of the double bond)

('*cis*' means 'one side'; '*trans*' means 'across'. The words come from Latin.)
To make sure you understand the difference between structural isomerism (page 15) and geometrical isomerism, you should attempt the next exercise.

EXERCISE 27

Answers on page 124

a There are three isomers with molecular formula $C_2H_2Cl_2$, two of which are shown below. Copy A and B and draw the third isomer (C).

b What type of isomerism exists in the following pairs?
i) A and B,
ii) A and C,
iii) B and C.
c Name the three isomers.
d State the differences between structural and geometrical isomerism.

You name some more geometrical isomers in the next exercise.

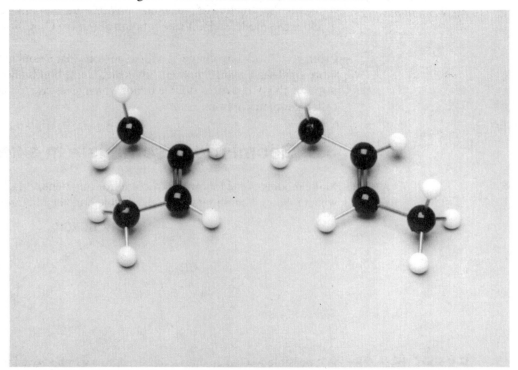

EXERCISE 28

Answers on page 124

a Give the names of

i)

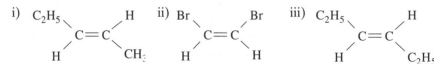

ii) Br   Br
       C=C
   H   H

iii) C_2H_5 H
         C=C
      H C_2H_5

b Give the structural formulae of
   i) *trans*-1, 2-dibromoethene,
   ii) *trans*-1-chloroprop-1-ene,
   iii) *cis*-hex-2-ene.

You now investigate some of the chemical properties of alkenes.

■ 3.4 Chemical properties of alkenes

OBJECTIVES

When you have finished this section you should be able to:
■ write equations for the **reactions of alkenes** stating the necessary conditions;
■ explain in general terms what takes place in an **addition reaction.**

You begin this section by comparing the strengths of the σ- and π-bonds in ethene in order to make a prediction about the reactivity of alkenes.

EXERCISE 29

Answers on page 124

a Calculate the C—C bond dissociation energy in ethane, C_2H_6, given the following information:

$$2C\,(g) + 6H\,(g) \rightarrow C_2H_6\,(g); \quad \Delta H^{\ominus} = -2820 \text{ kJ mol}^{-1}$$

$$\bar{E}(C—H) = 412 \text{ kJ mol}^{-1}$$

b Calculate the C=C bond dissociation energy in ethene, C_2H_4, given the following information:

$$2C\ (g) + 4H\ (g) \rightarrow C_2H_4\ (g); \quad \Delta H^\circ = -2260\ kJ\ mol^{-1}$$

c Assuming that the σ-bonds in ethane and ethene are identical (they are certainly very similar), calculate the approximate bond dissociation energy for the π-bond in ethene.
d Would you expect ethene to be more or less reactive than ethane?

You test your prediction in the next experiment, in which you repeat the procedure in Experiment 1 using an alkene instead of an alkane.

EXPERIMENT 2   Chemical properties of alkenes

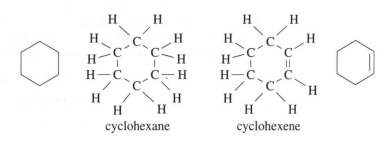

Aim   The purpose of this experiment is to test the reactivity of the alkenes by carrying out some test-tube reactions on cyclohexene.

Introduction   You will be using cyclohexene (which is a cycloalkene) because it is one of the cheapest liquid alkenes. It has virtually the same reactions as hexene and is similar to other alkenes. You will repeat the same reactions on cyclohexene that you performed on cyclohexane. This will enable you to compare the reactivities of the two types of hydrocarbon.

cyclohexane   cyclohexene

Requirements and Procedure

Turn to page 25 and work through the details of Experiment 1 again except that you substitute cyclohexene for cyclohexane. Record your results in another copy of the table under the heading Results Table 2.

HAZARD WARNING

Cyclohexene is an irritant. The vapour must not be inhaled. In the reaction between cyclohexene and concentrated sulphuric acid the amounts suggested must be strictly adhered to. Eye protection as usual and the front of the fume cupboard down as far as possible. All other precautions taken for Experiment 1 must also be adhered to here.

RESULTS
Specimen results on page 125

Questions
Answers on page 125

1. Was the prediction that you made in Exercise 29 verified by experiment?
2. Why do you think alkenes produce a sootier flame than alkanes?
3. Which test(s) could be used to distinguish between alkanes and alkenes?

The reactions of cyclohexene in Experiment 2 can be regarded as typical reactions of the C=C bond. In contrast with the alkanes, the alkenes are reactive compounds, tending to undergo addition reactions much more readily than substitution reactions.

■ 3.5 Addition reactions of alkenes

The addition reactions of alkenes can be summarised by the general equation in Fig. 4, which uses ethene as a typical alkene.

Figure 4

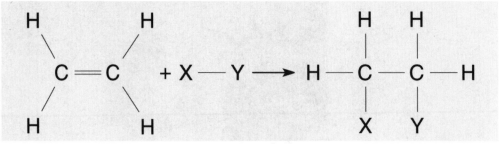

Read about the reactions of alkenes in your textbook(s). In addition to the reactions in Experiment 2, look for the reactions with hydrogen halides and hydrogen and for a simple account of the **polymerisation** of ethene. You will then be able to do the following exercises.

EXERCISE 30
Answers on page 125

Using Fig. 4 as a guide, complete the following equations for some addition reactions of a typical alkene, e.g. ethene. (These were illustrated in Experiment 2.) Add details of reaction conditions, i.e. whether the reaction takes place at room temperature or requires heat or a catalyst. State the name of the product in each reaction.

a $CH_2=CH_2 + Br_2 \rightarrow$

b $CH_2=CH_2 + H_2O + [O]* \rightarrow$

c $CH_2=CH_2 + H_2SO_4 \rightarrow X$; $X + H_2O \rightarrow$

*This is a simplified method of representing an oxidation reaction in organic chemistry. It is acceptable only when we wish to focus attention on the product rather than on electron transfer. Full equations may be obtained by combining the relevant half equations:

e.g. $C_2H_4 (g) + 2H_2O (l) \rightarrow C_2H_4(OH)_2 (l) + 2H^+ (aq) + 2e^-$

$MnO_4^- (aq) + 8H^+ (aq) + 5e^- \rightarrow Mn^{2+} (aq) + 4H_2O (l)$

Now you consider some further reactions which you did not illustrate in Experiment 2.

EXERCISE 31

Answers on page 125

Complete the following equations for the reactions of some alkenes. You should include details about reaction conditions and the names of the products.

a $CH_2{=}CH_2 + HBr \rightarrow$

b $CH_2CH{=}CHCH_3 + H_2 \rightarrow$

EXERCISE 32

Answers on page 125

In 1933, some scientists working at ICI were investigating the reactions of ethane with other carbon compounds under high pressure. In some of the experiments, the product was a hard waxy solid, which was found to consist only of carbon and hydrogen atoms in the ratio 1:2.

a What had the scientists discovered?

b Write an equation for the reaction which had taken place.

c Give the name of this type of reaction.

d What conditions are now used in industry for this reaction of ethene?

The product discovered in Exercise 32 above was a big molecule of the simplest type known as polymers. They consist of many identical units bonded together. Synthetic polymers are made by reactions between individual units (monomers) and we can classify them as addition or condensation polymers according to the type of reaction. Alkenes undergo addition polymerisation, which we now consider in a little more detail. You study condensation polymerisation later in ILPAC Volume 10, Big Molecules.

■ 3.6 Addition polymerisation

OBJECTIVES

When you have finished this section you should be able to:
■ show how many **addition polymers** are related to ethene, and write equations for the formation of some examples;
■ describe a **mechanism** for the formation of an addition polymer.

The most common type of addition polymer is based on ethene. One (or more) of the hydrogen atoms may be substituted by another group so that the generalised equation for the formation of an addition polymer where Y is the substituent is:

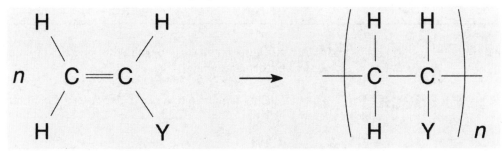

Find a textbook which covers addition polymers and skim the whole section. Look for a range of polymers that are substituted ethenes and the **free radical mechanism** for their formation. In particular, notice which substances act as catalysts in the reactions.

In the exercise which follows, you examine a range of addition polymers which are all substituted ethenes.

EXERCISE 33

Answers on page 126

Complete a larger copy of Table 10, which lists the side-chain groups found in the most common ethene-based polymers. Note that the trimers are included only to help you understand the structures – normally *n* = several hundreds or even thousands. Your everyday experience should enable you to include some uses of these polymers.

Table 10

Group Y in monomer $CH_2=CHY$	Structural formula of trimer ($n = 3$)	Repeating unit	Name(s) of polymer	Uses
—H	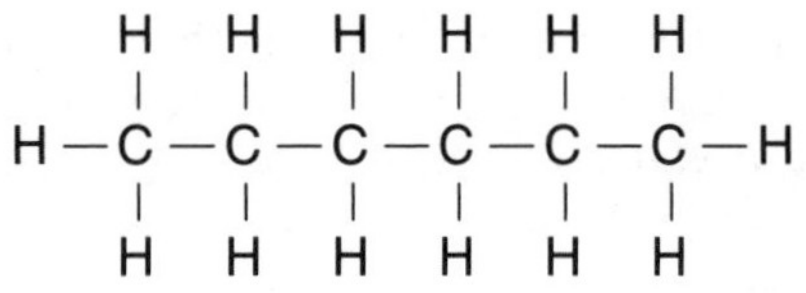 H—C—C—C—C—C—C—H (with H atoms above and below each C)	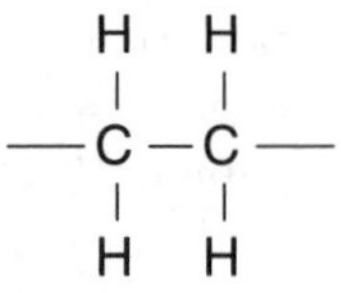 —C—C— (with H atoms above and below)	poly(ethene)	plastic bags, squeezy bottles, buckets, washing up bowls
—CH₃				
—Cl				
—CN				
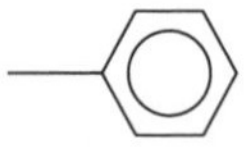 ⬡ (phenyl)				
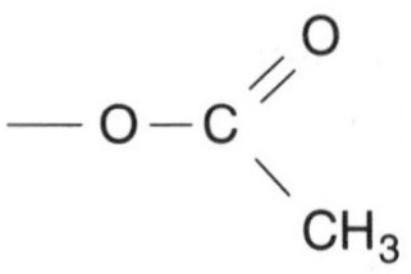 —O—C(=O)—CH₃				

In the next exercise you carry out the reverse process – deciding which monomer gives rise to a particular polymer.

EXERCISE 34

Answer on page 126

Which of the monomers **a** to **e** could give rise to the addition polymer shown below?

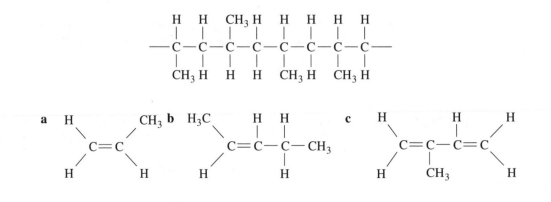

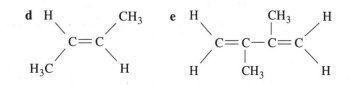

Many addition polymerisation reactions take place by a free radical mechanism. We explore such a reaction in the following Revealing Exercise. First check with your teacher to find out if you are required to study this on your particular syllabus.

EXERCISE

Revealing

Q1 Di(benzenecarbonyl) peroxide, often called benzoyl peroxide, has the formula:

It is commonly used as an initiator in chain reactions. The molecule can be split homolytically into two identical radicals. Write down the formula of the radical.

A1

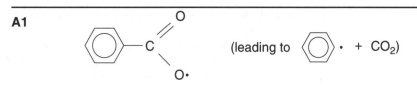

Q2 Using R• to stand for the radical, write an equation for the initiation step in the polymerisation of phenylethene (styrene). Assume that R• attacks the CH_2 group rather than the CH group.

A2

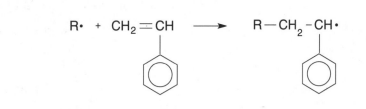

Q3 Write an equation to show how the product shown in A2 could react with another molecule of styrene.

A3

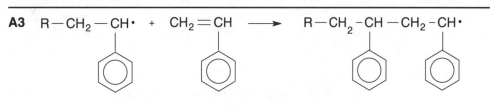

Q4 After any number of such propagation steps, the chain may be terminated in several different ways. State in words (no formulae) the types of particle which could react together in three possible termination steps.

A4 **a** Two initiating radicals.
  b A partly polymerised chain and an initiating radical.
  c Two partly polymerised chains.

Q5 Write an equation to show reaction **b**.

A5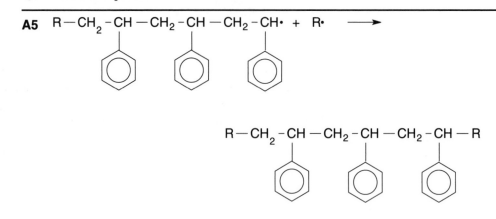

Q6 Why is the term 'catalyst' not strictly applicable to the initiator?

A6 Catalysts are regenerated in the course of a reaction.

Note that the presence of R groups at the ends of each chain means that the formula of the polymer is not completely represented by the formula $(-CH_2-CHC_6H_5-)_n$. However, the discrepancy is not important because n is so large.

We consider condensation polymerisation, physical properties of polymers in general and industrial methods of production in ILPAC Volume 10.

The reactions of alkenes are most often illustrated by reference to ethene. You should expect all other alkenes to undergo similar reactions, and they do. However, a problem arises when we try to decide the product of addition to unsymmetrical alkenes such as propene.

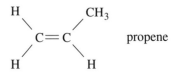 propene

In the section which follows, we show you how we make use of observations made by the scientist Markownikoff (pronounced 'Ma-*cough*-nick-off') to enable us to predict the major product in such reactions.

■ 3.7 Markownikoff's rule

OBJECTIVE When you have finished this section you should be able to:
■ use **Markownikoff's rule** to predict the product of addition to an unsymmetrical alkene.

If we add HBr to ethene there is only one possible product. It makes no difference which carbon atom accepts the bromine atom and which the hydrogen.

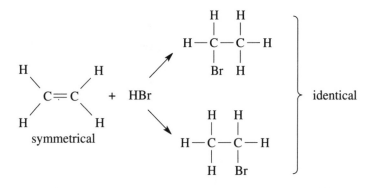

But with unsymmetrical alkenes such as propene there are two possible products.

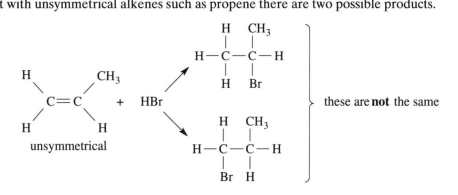

To decide which is the major product, we use Markownikoff's rule, which states:

'When a molecule adds across a double bond, the more electropositive atom or group adds to the carbon atom with more hydrogen atoms already attached'.

Very often, as in the example above, hydrogen is the more electropositive (less electronegative) atom and goes to the carbon with more hydrogen atoms, so we write:

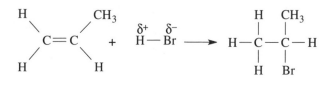

In general, you can predict the product of addition to an unsymmetrical alkene by applying Markownikoff's rule, provided you know how the added molecule splits into positive and negative parts. With this in mind, attempt the next exercise.

EXERCISE 35

Answers on page 126

Complete the following equations by drawing full structural formulae. Name the products:

a $CH_3CH=CH_2 + HBr \rightarrow$

b $CH_3CH=C(CH_3)_2 + HCl \rightarrow$

You now consider the mechanism for addition reactions of alkenes.

■ 3.8 Mechanism for addition in alkenes

In Experiment 2, you saw how cyclohexene and bromine react together even in the absence of light. A similar reaction occurs between ethene and bromine and since this reaction has been particularly well researched, we use it in our study.

OBJECTIVES

When you have finished this section you should be able to:
- ■ describe the **mechanism for addition in alkenes**;
- ■ describe the mechanism for Markownikoff addition in an unsymmetrical alkene.

Before we ask you to read about the mechanism for addition in alkenes, we describe some of the conventions which we use in writing mechanistic equations.

1. Reactant particles are drawn so that regions of high electron density are next to regions of electron deficiency. For instance, in representing the reaction between ammonia and hydrogen chloride, we write:

$$
\begin{array}{c}
\text{H} \\
| \\
\text{H}-\text{N:} \\
| \\
\text{H}
\end{array}
\quad
\overset{\delta+}{\text{H}}-\overset{\delta-}{\text{Cl}}
\quad \text{rather than} \quad
\begin{array}{c}
\text{H} \\
| \\
\text{H}-\text{N:} \\
| \\
\text{H}
\end{array}
\quad
\overset{\delta-}{\text{Cl}}-\overset{\delta+}{\text{H}}
$$

2. A curly arrow ⌢ is used to represent the movement of a **pair** of electrons during reaction.

In this example, the first arrow shows a lone pair on a nitrogen atom becoming a bonding pair between nitrogen and hydrogen atoms. The second arrow shows a bonding pair between hydrogen and chlorine atoms becoming a lone pair on a chloride ion. (The lone pairs are not always included in the formulae.)

3. A species which is formed in one step and destroyed in the next is called an intermediate. The formula of the intermediate is sometimes enclosed in square brackets.

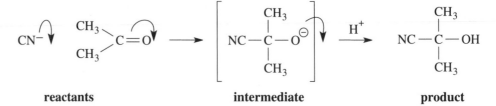

reactants   intermediate   product

4. A charge-sign, ⊕ or ⊖, is shown on any atom in the intermediate that has lost or gained control of an electron pair. In the example above, the oxygen atom has gained control of an electron pair and is given a negative charge.

Read about the reaction mechanism for the bromination of ethene in your textbook(s). This should include an account of the work of A. W. Francis. Look for an application of the conventions we have described above. Then you should be able to do the exercises which follow.

EXERCISE 36

Answers on page 127

a Complete a copy of the table below, making brief notes on each step of the mechanism for the bromination of ethene.

Table 11
Mechanism for the bromination of ethene

Step 1. Initiation	The bromine molecule becomes polarised as it approaches the region of high electron density in the double bond.
$Br — Br \longrightarrow \overset{\delta+}{Br} — \overset{\delta-}{Br}$	
Step 2. Formation of intermediate	
Step 3. Termination	

b Explain why the whole process described above is known as electrophilic addition.

In the Teacher-marked Exercise which follows, you use available evidence to confirm the proposed mechanism for the bromination of ethene.

EXERCISE

Teacher-marked

In 1925 the chemist A. W. Francis showed that when ethene is passed into an aqueous solution of bromine containing sodium chloride, one of the products is 1-bromo-1-chloroethane:

$$CH_2{=}CH_2 + Br_2 + Cl^- \text{ (aq)} \rightarrow CH_2BrCH_2Cl + Br^- \text{ (aq)}$$

How does this evidence support the mechanism for the bromination of ethene, proposed in Exercise 36?

The addition reactions of hydrogen halides, and sulphuric acid with alkenes are also known to take place by electrophilic addition, with similar mechanisms to that proposed for the bromination of ethene. You write mechanisms for these reactions in the next exercise.

EXERCISE 37

Answers on page 127

Suggest reaction mechanisms, like the one shown in Exercise 36, for the following reactions.

a $CH_2{=}CH_2 + H_2SO_4 \rightarrow CH_3CH_2OSO_2OH$

b $CH_2{=}CH_2 + HBr \rightarrow CH_3CHBr$

(Clue: H_2SO_4 polarises as $\overset{\delta^+}{H}{-}\overset{\delta^-}{OSO_2OH}$.)

We have already discussed the use of Markownikoff's rule in deciding the product of addition for unsymmetrical alkenes. We now give a mechanistic explanation for this rule in terms of the stability of carbocations.

■ 3.9 Markownikoff's rule and the stability of carbocations

OBJECTIVE

When you have finished this section you should be able to:
■ explain Markownikoff's rule in terms of the relative **stabilities** of primary, secondary and tertiary **carbocations**.

Consider the addition of hydrogen bromide to propene. Markownikoff's rule tells us that 2-bromopropane is the major product.

$$CH_3CH{=}CH_2 + HBr \nearrow \left[CH_3\overset{\oplus}{C}HCH_3 \right] \longrightarrow \boxed{\begin{array}{c} CH_3CHBrCH_3 \\ \text{2-bromopropane} \end{array}} \quad \text{major product}$$

$$\searrow \left[CH_3CH_2\overset{\oplus}{C}H_2 \right] \longrightarrow \begin{array}{c} CH_3CH_2CH_2Br \\ \text{1-bromopropane} \end{array}$$

The major product is 2-bromopropane because the intermediate carbocation $CH_3C^{\oplus}HCH_3$ is more stable than $CH_3CH_2C^{\oplus}H_2$, i.e. less energy is required to form $CH_3C^{\oplus}HCH_3$ than $CH_3CH_2C^{\oplus}H_2$. We can explain the difference in stability by considering the electron-releasing character of alkyl groups.

An alkyl group, such as $CH_3{-}$ or $C_2H_5{-}$, is said to be **electron-releasing** because the combined effect of the slightly polar C—H bonds tends to 'push' electrons towards the carbon atom to which the group is attached. This push (sometimes called an **inductive effect**) is represented in diagrams by an arrow in the centre of a bond-line, as shown below:

$$\overset{\delta^+}{H}\ \ \ \ \ \ \ \ \ \ \ \overset{\delta^+}{H}\ \overset{\delta^+}{H}$$
$$\overset{\delta^+}{H}{-}\underset{\underset{\delta^+}{H}}{\overset{|}{\underset{|}{C}}}{\longrightarrow} \quad \text{or} \quad CH_3{\longrightarrow} \qquad \overset{\delta^+}{H}{-}\underset{\underset{\delta^+}{H}}{\overset{|}{\underset{|}{C}}}{-}\underset{\underset{\delta^+}{H}}{\overset{|}{\underset{|}{C}}}{\longrightarrow} \quad \text{or} \quad C_2H_5{\longrightarrow}$$

An alkyl group in a carbocation therefore tends to stabilise the ion by effectively reducing the charge on the carbon atom. The overall positive charge becomes more 'spread out' over the ion (delocalised).

$$CH_3{\longrightarrow}\underset{\underset{H}{|}}{\overset{\overset{H}{|}}{\overset{\oplus}{C}}} \quad \text{and} \quad C_2H_5{\longrightarrow}\underset{\underset{H}{|}}{\overset{\overset{H}{|}}{\overset{\oplus}{C}}} \quad \text{are more stable than} \quad H{-}\underset{\underset{H}{|}}{\overset{\overset{H}{|}}{\overset{\oplus}{C}}}$$

Note that the electron-releasing effect of a single H atom is much smaller by comparison and is therefore not shown.

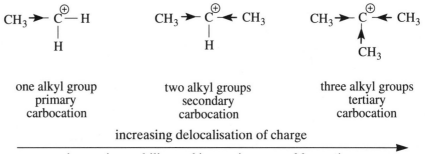

one alkyl group	two alkyl groups	three alkyl groups
primary	secondary	tertiary
carbocation	carbocation	carbocation

increasing delocalisation of charge
→
increasing stability and increasing ease of formation

To check your understanding of the previous sections, try the following exercise, which is a question from an A-level examination paper. We suggest that after reading the question and planning your answer, you write without further reference to your notes.

EXERCISE 38

Answers on page 128

2-Methylpropene, $(CH_3)_2C=CH_2$, reacts with HCl under certain experimental conditions to give almost entirely one organic product, although two might be expected.

a Write the formula of the expected major product and name it.

b Give a likely mechanism for the reaction in **a** and explain how it enables you to predict the formation of the expected major product.

In the next exercise, you describe the connection between the stability of carbocations and Markownikoff's rule.

EXERCISE 39

Answer on page 129

Use your answer from Exercise 38 to explain briefly why Markownikoff's rule works for the addition of HCl to 2-methylpropene.

You have now completed your study of the main reactions of alkenes. Before you go on to the next functional group, you should summarise and learn these reactions. This will make easier your study of other functional groups, because the same reactions will appear again as methods of preparation.

■ 3.10 Summary of reactions of alkenes

As you will soon begin to realise, your organic chemistry course requires you to learn many organic reactions. It is essential that you learn the reactions of a particular functional group before moving on to the next. A good way of learning reactions is to construct a summary chart, as indicated in the next exercise. Although you may have to write complete balanced equations, it is convenient in a summary to write abbreviated equations in the form:

$$\text{main reactant} \xrightarrow[\text{catalyst, conditions}]{\text{other reactant(s)}} \text{main product}$$

$$\text{e.g.} \quad CH_3CH=CH_2 \xrightarrow[\text{Ni, heat}]{H_2} CH_3CH_2CH_3$$

EXERCISE 40

Answers on page 129

Complete a copy of Fig. 5 to summarise the reactions of the alkenes.

Figure 5

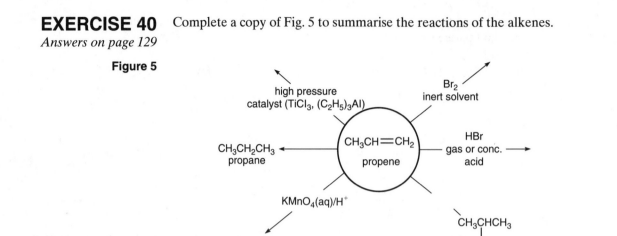

In order to test whether you have understood and learnt this section on alkenes you should attempt the following Teacher-marked Exercise. See if you can do it **without** referring to your notes.

EXERCISE

Teacher-marked

a i) Describe the nature of the bonding in simple alkenes, explaining how this governs their shape and chemical behaviour.

ii) State the most common type of reaction undergone by alkenes, the type of reagents with which they commonly react, and give **two** distinct examples of reactions of alkenes.

b Describe the mechanism and direction (orientation) of the addition of hydrogen bromide to propene.

c State the types of isomerism which exist in simple alkenes, sketch the structures of the four different isomeric forms of the alkene C_4H_8, and write the systematic names of **three** of them beneath the appropriate sketch.

There is another class of unsaturated hydrocarbons – the alkynes, which contain the C≡C bond. In many ways they are like alkenes, but they also have some distinctive properties. Since these compounds are now less important in synthetic routes we omit a detailed study of them from our course, as do most A-level syllabuses. Ethyne (acetylene) is the simplest alkyne and is still used in oxyacetylene welding.

Oxyacetylene welding.

We now look at a class of **aromatic** hydrocarbons – the arenes.

ARENES: C≡C BOND

The arenes are hydrocarbons whose molecules all contain a benzene ring. Arenes are examples of aromatic compounds.

OBJECTIVES

When you have finished the first part of this chapter you should be able to:
■ write the **general molecular formula** of the homologous series of **arenes** which contains **benzene**;
■ **name arenes.**

Read the introductory section on the arenes in your textbook. Look for the general molecular formula and names of arenes. In addition, refresh your memory on the **structure of benzene** from ILPAC Volume 3, Bonding and Structure.

EXERCISE 41

Answers on page 130

a Complete a copy of Table 12 which lists part of a homologous series of arenes.

Table 12

Name	Molecular formula	Structural formula
Benzene	C_6H_6	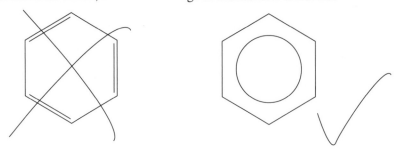
Methylbenzene		

b Write a general molecular formula for the homologous series of arenes shown in the table above.

c Use your data book to compare the melting points and boiling points of benzene and methylbenzene. Suggest reasons for the differences.

We have already discussed in detail the structure of benzene (ILPAC Volume 3, Bonding and Structure) and you know that the molecule does not have alternating single and double bonds, but uniform rings of delocalised electrons.

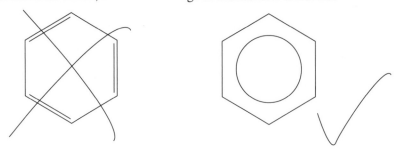

Each carbon–carbon bond is identical to the others and can be represented as C≡C. In the next exercise, you make a prediction about the reactivity of the C≡C bond.

EXERCISE 42

Answer on page 130

Would you expect the C≡C bond in benzene to be more or less susceptible to addition reactions than the C=C bond in alkenes? Explain your answer.

In ILPAC Volume 3 we suggested that, because the structure of benzene is a hybrid of electron-pair structures, it might have some of the character of alkanes and some of the character of alkenes as well as its own distinctive features. You can test this idea in the next section.

■ 4.1 Chemical properties of benzene

Scan the section of your textbook which deals with the chemical reactions of benzene. Read more carefully the parts you need to answer the questions in the following exercises.

Since benzene is suspected of being carcinogenic, we have omitted any practical work involving this compound. However, in order that you may test the prediction made in Exercise 42, we give you a set of specimen results for an experiment similar to those you have already done on alkanes and alkenes. Study the results and answer the questions which follow.

Results Table 3
Reactions of benzene –
specimen results

Reaction	Observations
A. **Combustion**	
Appearance of flame	Dark orange flame. Very sooty.
B. **Action of bromine** (in inert solvent)	
i) Dark.	i) Liquids mix. No reaction.
ii) Dark with iron powder. Identification of gas.	ii) Liquids mix. Brown colour fades rapidly. Steamy gas evolved. White fumes with ammonia – HBr.
iii) Light.	iii) Slight reaction – some decolorisation of bromine; no gas detectable.
C. **Action of acidified potassium manganate(VII)**	Liquids remain separate – no reaction.
D. **Action of concentrated sulphuric acid**	Liquids remain separate – no reaction. (Benzene will react with concentrated sulphuric acid but requires heat under reflux for several hours.)
E. **Action of concentrated nitric and sulphuric acids**	A yellow solution is formed fairly rapidly in the cold.

You should compare these results with the results you obtained for the reactions of alkanes and alkenes in Experiments 1 and 2.

EXERCISE 43
Answers on page 130

a Is the prediction you made in Exercise 42 verified by the observations in Results Table 3?
b Why does benzene produce a sootier flame than either cyclohexane or cyclohexene?
c Which of the reactions appears to be a substitution reaction? Is there any evidence of an addition reaction?
d Which experiments could you use to distinguish between:
   i) benzene and cyclohexane,
   ii) benzene and cyclohexene?

Most of the reactions of benzene are substitution reactions, as you will see in the following exercises. The first concerns reactions with halogens.

EXERCISE 44
Answers on page 131

a Write an equation for the substitution reaction of benzene with chlorine. Name the products and state the conditions.
b i) Write an equation for the addition reaction of benzene with chlorine. Name the product and state the conditions.
   ii) There are a number of geometric isomers of this addition product. Suggest a reason.
   iii) State a use for one of the geometric isomers.

The next exercise concerns substitution reactions with concentrated acids.

EXERCISE 45
Answers on page 131

a Write an equation for the reaction of benzene with concentrated sulphuric acid. Name the products and state the conditions.
b Write an equation for the reaction of benzene with concentrated nitric acid (mixed with concentrated sulphuric acid). Name the products and state the conditions.

EXERCISE 46
Answers on page 131

Suggest a reason for the fact that benzene, an unsaturated compound, does not readily undergo addition reactions.

We now consider the mechanisms for some of these substitution reactions.

■ 4.2 Mechanism of substitution reactions of benzene

OBJECTIVE

When you have finished this section you should be able to:
■ describe the **mechanism of substitution** reactions of benzene.

Read about the mechanisms for the **bromination of benzene** in the presence of a **halogen carrier** and for the **nitration of benzene**. Look for the equations for the preliminary reactions which produce the attacking species.

   In the next exercise, you use some available evidence to establish a mechanism for the substitution reactions of benzene.

EXERCISE 47
Answers on page 131

The chemists L. J. Lambourne and P. W. Robertson showed that when methoxybenzene reacts with iodine mono-chloride, only iodine substitution products are formed. For example,

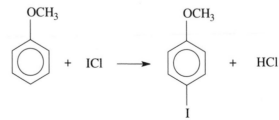

a Identify the attacking atom in this reaction.
b Which is the more electronegative atom, I or Cl?
c What does your answer above tell you about the charge on the attacking atom in this reaction?
d Use your answers above to help you outline a mechanism for this reaction and state the type of reaction taking place.

The answer to the last exercise, together with your reading, should help you to establish the mechanism for nitration and bromination of benzene.

EXERCISE 48
Answers on page 132

Benzene can be nitrated using a mixture of concentrated nitric acid and sulphuric acid.
a Name the attacking species present in the mixture of acids and write a balanced equation to represent its formation.
b What is the mechanism for the nitration of benzene? State the type of reaction taking place.

You now attempt a similar exercise for the bromination of benzene.

EXERCISE 49
Answers on page 132

Bromination of benzene can take place in the presence of iron filings.
a Name the attacking species in the bromination of benzene and write an equation for the reaction by which it is formed.
b Outline the mechanism for bromination of benzene and state the type of reaction taking place.
c Name the catalyst in this reaction and describe its function.

Two further electrophilic substitution reactions of benzene are known as **Friedel–Craft** reactions. Read about these reactions in your textbook(s) so that you can do the next exercise. You many find them referred to as **alkylation** and **acylation**.

EXERCISE 50
Answers on page 132

a Complete the following equations and name the products.

i) 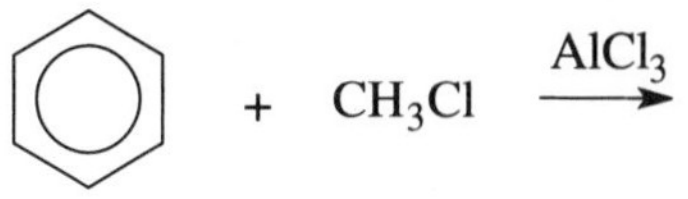
 + CH$_3$Cl $\xrightarrow{\text{AlCl}_3}$

ii) 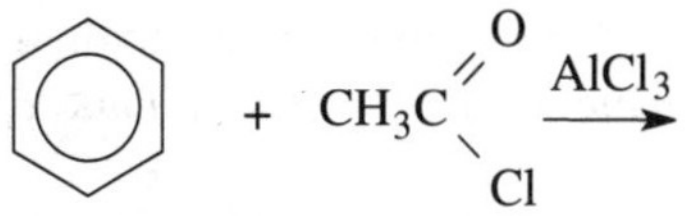
$\bigcirc$ + CH$_3$C$\underset{\text{Cl}}{\overset{\text{O}}{\diagdown}}$ $\xrightarrow{\text{AlCl}_3}$

b What names are given to each of the reactions shown above?
c Write mechanisms for reactions i) and ii) in part **a**. (Hint: the mechanisms are similar to that described for the bromination of benzene in the presence of the catalyst FeBr$_3$.)

Alkylbenzenes generally undergo similar reactions to those of benzene, but the presence of a side-chain makes further reactions possible, as you see in the next section.

■ 4.3 Reactions of alkylbenzenes

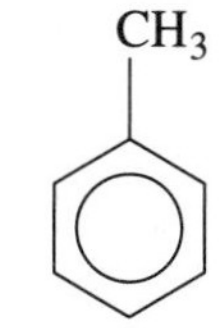

CH$_3$

methylbenzene

In alkylbenzenes, the benzene ring system has an alkyl group attached, e.g. the methyl group in methylbenzene. You should therefore expect these compounds to show a combination of arene and alkane reactions.

OBJECTIVES When you have finished this section you should be able to:
- describe how the side-branches in **alkylbenzenes** undergo **substitution** and **oxidation**;
- explain why **methylbenzene** is more readily nitrated than benzene.

Read about the **reactions of alkylbenzenes** such as methylbenzene (toluene) in your textbooks. Compare the reactions of the side-chain with typical alkane reactions, and the reactions of the benzene ring with those of benzene itself. You should then be able to do the following exercises.

When a halogen is passed into a boiling alkylbenzene such as methylbenzene in the presence of ultraviolet light, the methyl group is attacked before addition to the ring occurs. With this in mind, attempt the following exercise which is part of an A-level question.

EXERCISE 51
Answers on page 133

Dry chlorine was passed slowly into about 20 cm³ of boiling (under reflux) methylbenzene (toluene) contained in a flask irradiated with an ultraviolet lamp. The entire apparatus was set up in a fume cupboard and was covered completely with black paper.
i)   Give the structural formulae of the main products.
ii) What was the function of the ultraviolet light?
iii) Why was the apparatus covered with black paper?
iv) Suggest a mechanism for the reaction.
v)   Give two reasons for carrying out the experiment in a fume cupboard.

Compared with alkanes, the side-chain in alkylbenzenes is fairly easy to oxidise.

EXERCISE 52
Answer on page 134

Complete the following equation for the oxidation of the side-chain in methylbenzene.

CH₃

⬡ $\xrightarrow[\text{(heat)}]{\text{KMnO}_4/\text{H}^+ \text{ (aq)}}$

EXERCISE 53
Answer on page 134

Explain briefly why methylbenzene, $C_6H_5CH_3$, is more readily nitrated than benzene. (Clue: remember that an alkyl group is electron-donating, $CH_3 \rightarrow C$.)

Not only does the methyl group activate the ring towards the electrophile in comparison with benzene but it also directs the attacking electrophile predominantly into the 2, 4 and 6 positions of the ring. Extensive nitration of methylbenzene produces 2,4,6-trinitromethylbenzene, an important explosive known as TNT (trinitrotoluene).

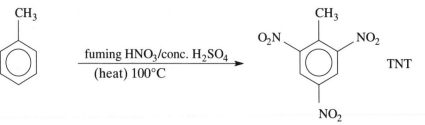

An explosion using TNT.

Other electrophilic substitution reactions of methylbenzene follow a similar pattern, as you can see in the next exercise.

EXERCISE 54
Answers on page 134

Predict the main products in the reaction between methylbenzene and chlorine in the presence of a halogen carrier.

You can now summarise the reactions of arenes.

■ 4.4 Summary of reactions of benzene and alkylbenzenes

EXERCISE 55

Answers on page 134

Complete a copy of Fig. 6 to summarise the reactions of benzene. Include those reactions of methylbenzene which involve the side-chain. (Remember that the other reactions of methylbenzene are very similar to those of benzene, but substitution occurs more readily.)

Figure 6
Summary of the reactions of arenes (benzene).

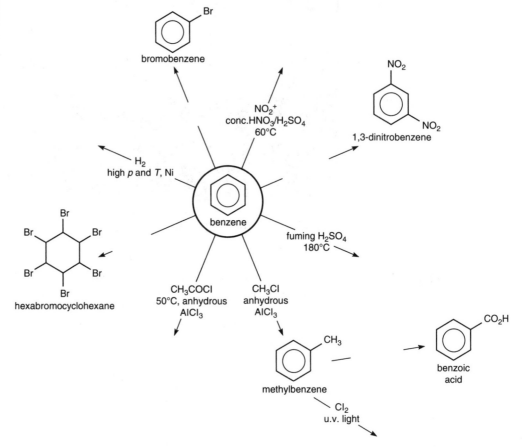

In order to test whether you have understood and learnt this section on arenes you should attempt the following Teacher-marked Exercise (**without** referring to your notes!). Since this exercise requires you to account for the stability of the benzene ring you should first revise this section from ILPAC Volume 3, Bonding and Structure.

EXERCISE

Teacher-marked

Write an account of the chemistry of the benzene ring. Your account should include the following:
a the nature and stability of the ring structure,
b the characteristic reactions of the benzene ring,
c the mechanisms of some of these reactions,
d why alkylbenzenes such as methylbenzene, $C_6H_5CH_3$, are more readily nitrated than benzene.

In the next section we consider how the hydrocarbons and some of their useful compounds are obtained directly or indirectly from petroleum. In addition, we mention briefly some of the economic and environmental factors related to the use of petroleum as an energy source.

PETROLEUM AND THE PETROCHEMICALS INDUSTRY

Petroleum, commonly called crude oil, is a complex mixture of hydrocarbons, which is used primarily to provide fuel, but also as a feedstock for the chemical industry.

OBJECTIVES

When you have finished the first part of this chapter you should be able to:
- outline two theories for the **origin of petroleum**;
- describe briefly how petroleum is **located**, **extracted** and **transported**;
- describe the process of **distillation** of petroleum and identify the different **fractions**.

An oil production platform in the North Sea.

Read about the likely origin of petroleum and how deposits are located. Look for a simple account of the extraction of petroleum and the first stage in **refining** it, namely **fractional distillation**. You should then be able to do the following exercise. (If your textbook does not cover these topics adequately, ask your teacher for some of the booklets produced by the major oil companies.)

EXERCISE 56

Answers on page 135

a Two theories have been put forward to explain the origins of petroleum. What are they?

b Name three methods a geologist might use to search for oil.

c About 80–90% of the known petroleum resources occur in either anticlines or faults. Explain, with diagrams, how these rock structures trap oil.

d In drilling for oil, a specially prepared fluid, called 'drilling mud', is forced down the drill pipe under great pressure. Give three reasons for this.

EXERCISE 57

Answers on page 135

Figure 7 shows the main oil movements by sea in 1989. Study it and attempt the questions which follow.

Figure 7
Crude oil seaborne trade, 1989.

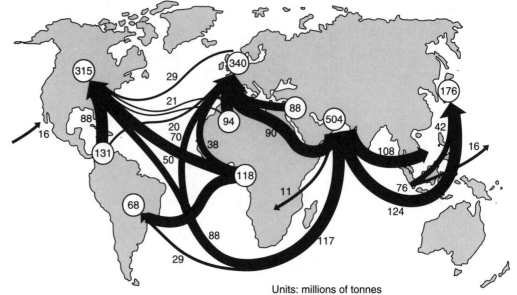

Units: millions of tonnes

a From which area does Europe obtain most of its petroleum?
b How do you think the closing of the Suez Canal in 1956 affected the movement of petroleum to Europe?
c What led to the development of very large tankers, called supertankers, for transporting petroleum?
d A considerable amount of Europe's oil imports from the Middle East come around Africa despite the fact that the Suez Canel has been open since the mid-1970s. Why do you think this is?

Once crude oil has been located and extracted, it must be transported to a refinery where it is processed. The first process in oil refining is distillation, which is the subject of the next exercise.

EXERCISE 58

Answers on page 136

Copy Fig. 8 and label the parts A to F as you answer the questions which follow.

Figure 8
Distillation of crude oil.

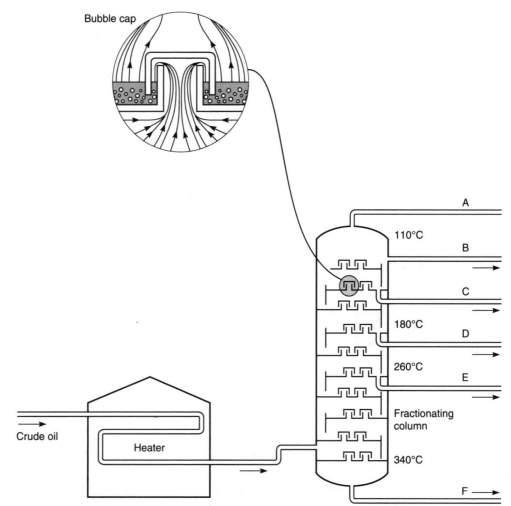

a The main fractions into which crude oil can be separated by distillation are gasoline (petrol), kerosene (paraffin oil) residues, diesel oil, naphtha and refinery gas. Identify each of these fractions with the letters in the diagram. State approximately the average number of carbon atoms per molecule of hydrocarbon in each fraction.
b Briefly explain the function of the horizontal trays and bubble caps inside the fractionating column.
c Fraction F is piped away and is further separated by vacuum distillation. Name the fractions obtained by this process.
d State the main uses of each of the fractions shown.
e Up to the turn of this century, the only oil fraction required in quantity was kerosene; the other fractions were wasted. Later, the demand switched from kerosene to gasoline. More recently, however, kerosene has again been required in great quantities. Discuss briefly the reasons for these changes in demand.

Petrol is one of the main end-products of crude oil. Using the gasoline fraction to supply the huge demand for petrol would lead to the other fractions being overproduced. One way of solving this problem is to break down the large molecules in heavier fractions into smaller more useful ones. This is achieved through the chemical processes of cracking, reforming, alkylation and isomerisation, which you study in the next section.

■ 5.1 The composition of blended petrol

OBJECTIVES

When you have finished this section you should be able to:
■ explain what is meant by **catalytic cracking**, **catalytic reforming**, **alkylation** and **isomerisation**;
■ explain why these processes are important in the manufacture of high-grade motor fuel;
■ explain the meaning of the term **octane number**;
■ explain why tetraethyl lead(IV), $(C_2H_5)_4Pb$, is added to petrol and why legislation is restricting this practice.

Read about the importance of the processes described in the objectives above from a suitable textbook or pamphlet. Your teacher should be able to suggest some booklets from oil companies. You should also look out for the meaning of the term octane number and the advantages and disadvantages of adding tetraethyl lead to petrol. You should then be able to do the next comprehension exercise.

EXERCISE 59

Answers on page 136

Read the passage below and answer the questions which follow.

Octane number of petrol hydrocarbons

When it is first obtained from the Earth, crude oil is a complex mixture of hydrocarbons with sulphur compounds and inorganic impurities. The hydrocarbons may contain between one and more than fifty carbon atoms, and are mostly alkanes (with straight or branched chains), together with naphthenes and arenes. Petroleum is separated into fractions by distillation, for example, gasoline, naphtha, kerosine, gas oil, and diesel oil.

In general, the percentage of motor gasoline or petrol in crude oils is not enough to meet the heavy demands for motor car use. So it is necessary to devise ways whereby a larger proportion of the hydrocarbons in crude oil can be made use of as petrol. The value of hydrocarbons for use in petrol can be judged from their 'octane number'. Heptane is given an octane number of 0 and 2,2,4-trimethylpentane (iso-octane) is given an octane number of 100. The higher the number, the less tendency to pre-ignite in a car engine, that is, the less tendency to explode under compression before the spark is passed. A second explosion when the spark is passed results in the two shock waves producing a characteristic 'knocking' in the engine.

Figure 9
One of the cylinders
of a car engine.

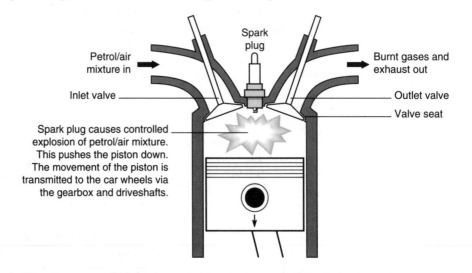

The processes of importance for producing petrol-grade hydrocarbons are catalytic cracking, catalytic reforming, and alkylation.

Catalytic cracking One method of obtaining more petrol is to heat the larger hydrocarbon molecules so that they break down. In early years the process of thermal cracking was used, although much of the petroleum was broken down too extensively. In the 1930s, the higher compression in petrol engines called for fuels with a higher octane rating. The value for the products of thermal cracking was only 70–80. Fortunately, it had been discovered that the cracking of hydrocarbons in the presence of a catalyst (catalytic cracking) gave a petrol containing more branched hydrocarbons and an octane rating of 90–95.

Nowadays, crystalline aluminosilicates, known as zeolites or molecular sieves, are used as cracking catalysts.

Catalytic reforming This is now one of the most important processes for the production of motor gasolines. Adding a metallic component to a cracking catalyst gives petrol with an even higher octane number. Platinum is used exclusively as this component and highly purified alumina is used in place of silica-alumina. The process is known as catalytic reforming, but 'platforming' and other commercial names are often used.

The improvement in octane number is due largely to the higher percentage of arenes in the product. The process is also a source of arenes for the chemical industry. Some of the chemical reactions which are carried out at the same time by reforming catalysts are:

■ dehydrogenation of cyclohexanes to arenes,
■ dehydrocyclisation of alkenes and alkanes to arenes,
■ isomerisation of unbranched chain alkanes to branched chain alkanes,
■ hydrocracking to hydrocarbons of lower relative molecular mass.

In a reforming catalyst, the platinum is highly dispersed over the alumina, perhaps as platinum atoms or small groups of atoms. Both the platinum and alumina play a catalytic role.

Alkylation Another means of obtaining high octane blending stocks is to join some of the smaller molecules in the right way, that is, using C_3–C_4 hydrocarbons. The process of alklyation involves the reaction of a branched chain-alkane (for example, 2-methyl-propane) and an alkene (for example, propene or butene). The catalysts are, or contain, acids; sulphuric acid, hydrofluoric acid, and phosphoric acid are used.

Octane number and molecular structure
The octane number of different hydrocarbons is shown in Table 13.

Table 13	Hydrocarbon	Structure	Octane number
	Heptane		0
	Hexane		26
	2-Methylhexane		41
	Cyclohexane		77
	2,2-Dimethylpentane		89
	2,2,4-Trimethylpentane		100
	Benzene		108
	Methylbenzene		124

The reason that changes in molecular structure enhance octane number lies in the process of combustion. The conditions of temperature and pressure in a car engine result in the production of free radicals. The more reactive the free radicals, the greater the chance of an uncontrolled chain reaction such as pre-ignition explosion or knocking in the engine. Branched alkane free radicals are less reactive than unbranched. The function of the petrol additive, tetraethyl lead, is to help to control the free radical chain reaction. When free radicals react with tetraethyl lead the chain is terminated because the final product is an unreactive lead atom.

a i) What is meant by pre-ignition?
   ii) How is the octane number related to pre-ignition?
b i) Complete a copy of Table 13 by including the structural formula for each compound.
   ii) Which types of compound in Table 13 cause the least amount of knocking?
c Explain the difference between catalytic cracking and catalytic reforming.
d i) By what process is ethene manufactured from fractions obtained from crude petroleum?
   ii) Give a balanced equation to show how ethene might be formed from $C_{14}H_{30}$ in this process.
e Write an equation to show hexadecane, $C_{16}H_{34}$, being cracked into two smaller octane molecules (clue: something else is needed to balance the equation and the process is called hydrocracking).
f Write an equation for the catalytic reforming of the following and say whether the product will have a higher or lower octane number than the reactants.
   i) Hexane to cyclohexane,
   ii) cyclohexane to benzene.
g One of the products in parts **f** i) and ii) above is hydrogen. Suggest the process which could make use of this.
h Suggest an equation for one possible isomerisation of the alkane $CH_3(CH_2)_5CH_3$ and say whether the product will have a higher or lower octane number than the reactant.
i i) What is a free radical?
   ii) Write an equation for the formation of two free radicals from 2,2,4-trimethyl-pentane (each containing four carbon atoms). Is homolytic or heterolytic fission involved?
   iii) Write an equation for the formation of two propyl free radicals from hexane.
   iv) Which of the reactions in ii) and iii) above gives products which will cause the most knocking?
   v) Complete the following equation for the reaction between tetraethyl lead(IV) and a propyl free radical and use it to explain why tetraethyl lead(IV) is added to petrol.

$$(CH_3CH_2)_4Pb \quad + \quad 4 \cdot \overset{\overset{\textstyle CH_3}{\textstyle |}}{CH} - CH_3 \quad \longrightarrow$$

   vi) What could be done to improve the overall octane rating of petrol without the need to add lead additives?
j Why has legislation restricted the addition of tetraethyl lead(IV) to petrol in many countries?

Figure 10
An unleaded petrol pump.

Table 14 summarises the restrictions which have been imposed on the use of tetraethyl lead in petrol in the U.K. In view of this legislation we should have expected to see a significant drop in airborne lead concentrations. In the exercise which follows you analyse data to find out if this is the case.

Table 14	1972	Maximum lead levels reduced to 0.83 grams per litre.
	1985	EU legislation restricted lead levels to 0.4 grams per litre.
	1986	Lead levels in Britain reduced to 0.15 grams per litre well in advance of EU guideline date of 1989.
	1989	EU guidelines stipulated that unleaded petrol must be available with an octane number of 95.
	1993	All new cars were to be fitted with catalytic converters, which could be used only with unleaded petrol.

EXERCISE 60
Answers on page 139

Figure 11 shows the annual average lead concentrations at two different sites in the U.K. Figure 12 shows unleaded petrol as a percentage of total deliveries. Study them along with the information in Fig. 15 on page 67 and attempt the questions which follow.

Figure 11
Lead in petrol monitoring sites in U.K.: annual average concentrations in the air (1985–1991).

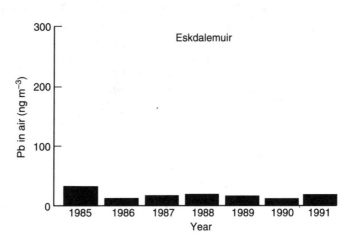

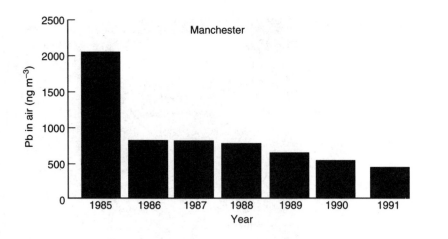

Figure 11 (Continued).

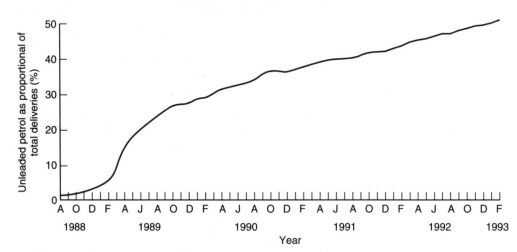

Figure 12
Unleaded petrol as a
percentage of total delivery.

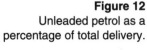

a How do you account for the general difference in airborne lead levels at the two sites?

b Describe the effect the various restrictions on lead additives have had on airborne lead levels.

c When do you think the government launched an effective campaign to encourage drivers to use unleaded petrol?

d Catalytic converters are cylinders containing catalysts which are fitted to car exhausts to remove nitrogen oxides and carbon monoxide. Explain why they can be fitted only to cars which run on lead-free petrol.

e What effect do you think the 1993 legislation will have on the levels of airborne lead over the ten or so years which follow?

Although lead compounds are the most economical anti-knock additives (octane boosters) they are, as we have seen, certainly not the most environmentally friendly. However, even unleaded fuels cause problems. To achieve an acceptable octane number, aromatic compounds such as benzene are often added and, as you learnt earlier in the chapter, some of these are quite toxic themselves. Exposure to high concentrations of benzene has been implicated as a cause of leukaemia. The 1993 legislation requiring all new cars to be fitted with a catalytic converter should bring down these levels. We shall look at catalytic converters in a later section, which considers the wider topic of air pollution resulting from burning fossil fuels, such as coal and oil, in the home, industry or the internal combustion engine.

■ 5.2 The petrochemicals industry

The petrochemicals industry began with an attempt to make use of some of the gaseous waste products from certain refinery processes, notably cracking. Since 1918, the industry has grown to such an extent that almost all the world's production of organic chemicals comes from petroleum.

We cannot possibly deal with the whole range of petrochemicals in this volume. Instead we suggest you concentrate on some of the important products manufactured from ethene and propene. (The butenes are also important as starting materials and so are the arenes, benzene and methylbenzene. In the U.K., the arenes are made by catalytic cracking and reforming of petroleum fractions.)

■ 5.3 Chemicals from ethene and propene

You already know some of the reactions of ethene and propene under laboratory conditions. The conditions employed in industry are often very different; the emphasis is on cheap raw materials even if this means operating at high temperatures and pressures. It can also be economical to use very expensive catalysts in large-scale production.

Figure 13
An industrial chemical plant.

OBJECTIVE   When you have finished this section you should be able to:
■ write equations to show how **ethene** and **propene** are converted into many useful compounds.

Use your textbook to find out how ethene and propene can be converted into useful chemicals on the industrial scale. Also find out how cereal grain may be used as an alternative industrial preparation of ethanol. This will enable you to do the following exercises.

EXERCISE 61
Answers on page 139

Grain may be used as a raw material for the industrial preparation of ethanol.
a   State the process involved and name the compound which is converted into ethanol.
b   State the gaseous by-product of the process.
c   Today most industrial ethanol is manufactured by the direct catalytic hydration of ethene in the vapour phase.

$$CH_2{=}CH_2 \text{ (g)} + H_2O \text{ (g)} \xrightarrow[\text{on celite 300°C, 60 atm}]{H_3PO_4} \underset{\text{ethanol}}{CH_3CH_2OH} \text{ (g)}$$

Give **one** advantage and **one** disadvantage of the grain-based process for the production of ethanol over that using ethene.

d Name the industrial uses of ethanol.

Ethanol is not the only product obtained from ethene as you see in the next exercise.

EXERCISE 62

Answers on page 139

Ethene is frequently called 'the building-block chemical'.

a State the reactants and conditions for the manufacture of the following compounds from ethene, C₂H₄:
i) ethane-1,2-diol,
ii) chloroethene (vinyl chloride),
iii) polyethene,
iv) phenylethene (styrene).

b Name a commercial outlet for each of the products described in part **a** i)–iv).

EXERCISE 63

Answers on page 140

a State the reactants and conditions which are necessary for bringing about the conversions shown in Fig. 14.

b State a commercial use for each of the six products shown in Fig. 14.

Figure 14
Industrial chemicals from propene.

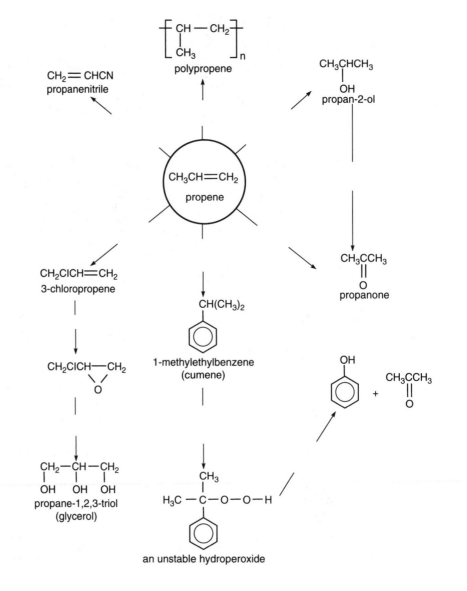

Petroleum is not the only source of supply of fuel or chemical feedstock. Since the tremendous rise in price of petroleum in the early 1970s and the worries about its rate of consumption, more attention has been focused on natural gas and coal. You will study industrial processes and the factors that influence the design of chemical process plants later in the series.

■ 5.4 Looking ahead

OBJECTIVE   When you have finished this section you should be able to:
■ discuss the world's **energy requirements** in relationship to the supplies available and to the needs of the petrochemical industry.

In the next exercise, you compare the consumption of petroleum as a source of energy with coal, natural gas and hydro/nuclear electricity.

EXERCISE 64

Answers on page 141

Figure 15 shows the energy consumption in the U.K. since 1950. Study it and attempt the questions which follow.

Figure 15
U.K. consumption of energy
1950–1992.

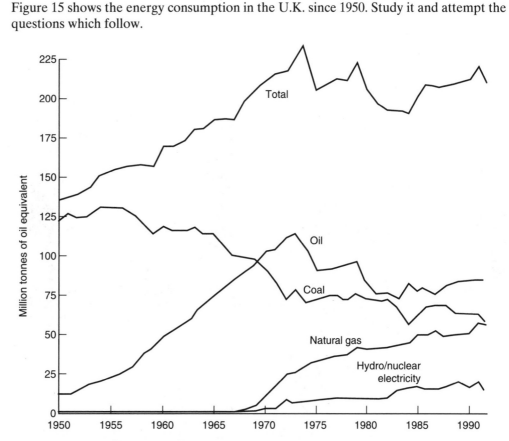

a Compare the trends in the consumption of petroleum and coal in the U.K. since 1950 and account for the difference.
b How do you account for the sudden increase in the consumption of natural gas in the U.K.?
c Has the increased price of petroleum had any effect on its consumption since the late 1970s?

The world consumption of different forms of energy shows a similar trend to that in the U.K. The world has therefore become increasingly dependent on oil, which is now the primary source of energy.

In the next two exercises, you consider how this situation might change in view of the life expectancy of the different sources.

EXERCISE 65

Answers on page 141

Figure 16 shows the production and reserves of oil for the year ending 1992. (Crude oil reserves are generally taken to be the **known** oil deposits which we can reasonably expect to recover in the future under **existing** economic and operating conditions.) Study the data and attempt the questions which follow.

Figure 16
Total oil discoveries.

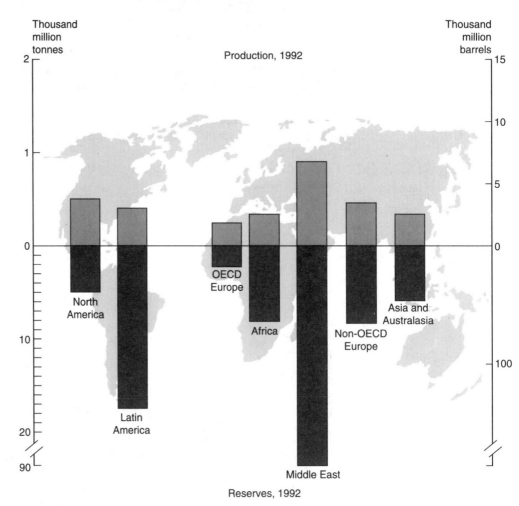

a Where are the world's major oil reserves?

b If production 'at the rate for 1992' were to continue, calculate the date when reserves might be expected to run out in the Middle East.

It is interesting to compare the predicted life of oil with that for natural gas and coal. You do this in the next exercise.

EXERCISE 66

Answers on page 141

Table 15 shows the world production and reserves for petroleum, natural gas and coal respectively for 1992. Study it and attempt the questions which follow.

Table 15
(rate in thousand million tonnes oil equivalent)

Fossil fuel	Reserves	1992 production
Crude oil	137	3.2
Natural gas	127	1.8
Coal	510	2.2

a Estimate how long the reserves of oil, natural gas and coal will last at the 1992 rate of consumption.
b Estimate the reserves of each fossil fuel as a percentage of total reserves.
c How do you think the relative consumption of different energy sources will change over the next fifty or so years?
d Suggest two reasons why the predictions you have made on the life of various resources may not be correct.

Forward predictions are often notoriously inaccurate. Nevertheless, in view of the relatively short life expectancy of petroleum and natural gas deposits, it is prudent to make contingency plans for our future requirements of energy and chemicals.

 Read as widely as you can, in newspaper and magazine articles as well as books and pamphlets, about the different ways of satisfying future demands for energy and chemicals. You should then be able to attempt the following Teacher-marked Exercise.

EXERCISE

Teacher-marked

Discuss the following statements critically:
■ 'Predictions of doom, by experts or others, have three things in common. They assume fixed resources; they assume fixed technology; and they have so far proved to be false. In 1891, the United States Geological Survey declared that there was little or no oil in Texas. In 1914, the United States Bureau of Mines estimated that oil output would be six thousand million barrels in the whole history of the country. This amount is now produced every 18 months'. (Arthur Schenfield, a former economic director of the Confederation of British Industry.)
■ 'Oil is too valuable a material to be burned, and should be reserved as a source of chemicals'. (Mendeleev reporting to his government after a visit to America in **1872**.)
■ 'The prospect facing the energy doom-watcher is, therefore, a curious one – political in essence. Leaving pollution to one side, the problem is not to avoid a slide into a world starved and depleted of its energy sources, but how to get through the next thirty years – which are beginning to look like a petroleum-dominated transition period between coal and nuclear power'. (Joe Roeber, *The Times*, 1 February 1972).

One positive outcome which will result from dwindling supplies of fossil fuels is a drop in the levels of air pollutants which result from their combustion.

In the U.K., the Clean Air Act of 1956 succeeded in cleaning up some of the country's most obvious air pollution problems, such as the infamous smogs of the 1950s, which killed thousands of people. Nevertheless the combustion of fossil fuels for heating, cooking and transport continues to threaten human life and the environment. Although the polluting gases are invisible with no smell, they are nevertheless linked with problems such as asthma and bronchitis and more widely with the depletion of the ozone layer, the 'greenhouse effect' and acid rain. You consider these problems in the next chapter.

AIR POLLUTION

This chapter covers air pollution resulting from burning fossil fuels. You consider the sources of the pollutants, their effect on the environment and health, and some methods to control them. After an introductory exercise on all air pollutants in general, you go on to study each one in more detail under separate headings.

■ 6.1 Air pollutants

OBJECTIVE   When you have finished this section you should be able to:
■ identify the **air pollutants** from burning fossil fuels and their effects.

 Read about the source and effects on health and the environment from the pollutants which result from burning fossil fuels. You should then be able to do the following exercise. If your textbook does not cover these topics adequately ask your teacher for some of the booklets produced by Friends of the Earth and others.

EXERCISE 67   Complete a copy of Table 16 which lists the main pollutants which result from burning
Answers on page 142   fossil fuels.

Table 16

Pollutant	Sulphur dioxide	Hydrocarbons	Carbon monoxide	Ozone	Nitrogen oxides
Source		Unburnt hydrocarbons from exhaust emissions, emissions during refuelling and distribution of fuels		In the lower atmosphere formed by a photochemical reaction involving nitrogen oxides, oxygen and sunlight	
Health effects		Aromatics can be carcinogens. Benzene has been linked with leukaemia		Beneficial in the the upper atmosphere but harmful at ground level. High concentrations can damage lung tissue and the immune system. Aggravates asthma and bronchitis	
Environmental effects			Oxidises to carbon dioxide, the greenhouse gas	Major component of 'photochemical smog'; damages plastics, rubber, paints and crops by reducing yields	

We now consider the effects of carbon dioxide, formerly not regarded as a pollutant but now causing concern.

6.2 Carbon dioxide and the 'greenhouse effect'

Carbon dioxide has for many years been considered the cause of the 'greenhouse effect', whereby the temperature of the earth is steadily rising. You now consider how this arises, the consequences and possible solutions.

OBJECTIVE

When you have finished this section you should be able to:
■ discuss the way in which increased concentrations of **carbon dioxide** and other greenhouse gases contribute to **global warming** and the measures which could reduce it.

Read as widely as you can, in newspaper and magazine articles as well as books and pamphlets, about the effects of increased levels of carbon dioxide and other greenhouse gases on our climate. You should then be able to attempt the following Teacher-marked Exercise.

EXERCISE
Teacher-marked

A lot of people talk about the greenhouse effect but don't really know what causes it. Write a report which clearly and simply explains:
a what the greenhouse effect is,
b what the consequences are,
c what we can do about it.

We now consider sulphur dioxide emissions in more detail and measures which can be taken to reduce them.

6.3 Sulphur dioxide and acid rain

Sulphur dioxide is responsible for about 70% of the acidity of rainfall. Acid rain has been falling for well over a hundred years but the damaging effects are only now becoming apparent. In this section you analyse data to determine the major source of sulphur dioxide pollution and then consider ways of reducing it.

OBJECTIVES

When you have finished this section you should be able to:
■ explain the changes in **levels of sulphur dioxide** in the air since 1850;
■ identify the major **source of sulphur dioxide** pollution by emission source and type of fuel;
■ describe methods which might be employed to **minimise sulphur dioxide** emissions.

In the next exercise you consider why SO_2 levels have changed over the past 140 years.

EXERCISE 68
Answers on page 143

Figure 17 shows the levels of SO_2 over the past 140 years. Study it together with Fig. 15 (on page 67) and attempt the questions which follow.

Figure 17
Sulphur dioxide levels
in the air, 1840–1990.

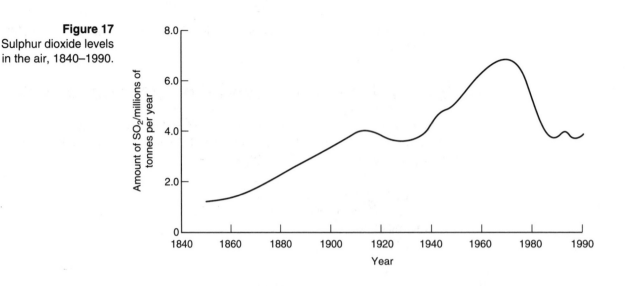

a Suggest reasons for the changes in SO$_2$ emissions in the following years:
  i)   1850–1900,
  ii) 1920–1930,
  iii) 1940–1960,
  iv) 1970–1990.
b Most of the SO$_2$ produced rises into the atmosphere and is carried by winds to create
  acid rain many hundreds of miles away. The reactions involved in producing acid rain
  are quite complex and involve free radicals. Complete the following equations which
  represent a possible sequence:

$$OH\bullet + SO_2 + O_2 \rightarrow HO_2\bullet + \,?$$

$$? + H_2O \rightarrow H_2SO_4$$

EXERCISE 69

Answers on page 143

Tables 17 and 18 list SO$_2$ emissions by source and type of fuel in 1980 and 1991. Study
them and attempt the questions which follow.

Table 17
SO$_2$ estimated
emissions by source
(thousand tonnes)

Emission source	1980	1991
Domestic	226	133
Commercial/public	197	83
Power stations	3007	2534
Refineries	237	115
Agriculture	21	8
Other industry	1093	569
Railways	11	3
Road transport	42	58
Civil aircraft	2	2
Shipping	62	61
Total	4898	3566

Fuel	1980	1991
Coal fuel	3229	2785
Solid smokeless fuel	64	47
Petroleum motor fuel	11	17
DERV (diesel fuel)	30	41
Gas oil	121	58
Fuel oil	1378	573
Burning oil	2	1
Other petroleum	27	25
Other emissions	35	18
Total	4897	3565

Table 18
SO_2 estimated emissions by type of fuel (thousand tonnes)

a Which source accounts for most of the SO_2 emissions?
b Which two fuels account for most of the SO_2 emissions?
c Calculate the percentage drop in emissions of SO_2 between 1980 and 1991.

The effect of acid rain at Mynydd Dinas near Port Talbot.

An EU directive has set emission limits for SO_2 in combustion plants with capacity greater than 50 megawatts that there should be a 40% reduction by 1998 and 60% by 2003, taking 1980 as the baseline. In the exercise which follows you look at the various methods available for achieving these targets.

EXERCISE 70
Answers on page 143

a If present trends continue and no changes are made do you think the EU 1998 and 2003 targets for large combustion plants which include power stations will be achieved?
b A number of options exist for cleaning up acid gases; some are listed below. Study them, think about the consequences and draw up a list of the advantages and disadvantages of implementing each. You may like to discuss this as a group activity.

A row of electricity generating
wind turbines near Leylstad,
The Netherlands.

- **Increased use of nuclear power**
- **Change from coal- to gas-fired power stations**
- **Increase the energy we get from renewable sources** (an increase of 20% of total energy has been suggested as possible over the next 20 years)
- **Increased energy efficiency** (recent government figures show we could reduce the energy used in the U.K. by 60%)
- **Install flue gas desulphurisation plants (FGDs)** (which can remove up to 90% of the SO_2 in waste gases by passing through limestone)

Ratcliff-on-Soar power station
showing flue gas
desulphurisation plant on the
right-hand side.

One way of tackling the acid rain problem is to pass the waste gases containing sulphur dioxide through an aqueous suspension of limestone. In the next exercise you estimate the quantities of materials involved.

EXERCISE 71

Answers on page 144

a Describe the changes you would expect to see when sulphur dioxide is passed through an aqueous suspension of limestone. The overall reaction is:

$$2SO_2 + 2CaCO_3 + O_2 = 2CaSO_4 + 2CO_2$$

b The 2000 MW coal-fired power station at Ratcliff-on-Soar in Nottingham has been identified as one of the dirtiest power stations in Britain and will now be fitted with a FGD (flue gas desulphurisation) plant to remove up to 90% of the SO_2 from its waste gas. Assuming this plant uses on average 10,000 tonnes of limestone a week, calculate:
   i)   the mass of SO_2 that could be removed each week (1 tonne = 1×10^6 g).
   ii) the mass of gypsum $CaSO_4 \cdot 2H_2O$ that will be produced each week.
   iii) the mass of CO_2 produced if 1.2×10^5 tonnes of coal are burnt each week.
        (Assume the coal is just carbon.)
   iv) The mass of CO_2 produced by the FGD process.
c Suggest ways you think Powergen might dispose of the calcium sulphate. (Look up the uses of calcium sulphate in an inorganic textbook.)
d Compare your answers to parts **b** iii) and iv) above and decide if the FGD process will contribute significantly to the greenhouse effect.

We now look at another gas, this time ozone, which is an essential natural gas in the upper atmosphere but a pollutant causing photochemical smogs in the lower atmosphere.

■ 6.4 Ozone – friend or foe?

Ozone has a dual action. Within our environment too much man-made ozone in the lower atmosphere is a pollutant as illustrated in Fig. 18, whilst not enough natural ozone in the upper atmosphere (Fig. 19) leaves us unprotected from harmful ultraviolet radiation from the sun.

Figure 18
Photochemical smog.

Figure 19
Antarctic ozone depletion.
The large clear central oval
represents the 'ozone hole'.
Compiled from data from the
Russian Meteor-3 satellite.

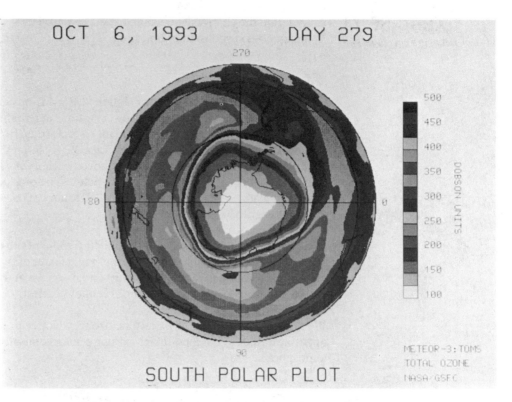

OCT 6, 1993   DAY 279

270

180

0

90

SOUTH POLAR PLOT

500
450
400
350
300
250
200
150
100

DOBSON UNITS

METEOR-3:TOMS
TOTAL OZONE
NASA/GSFC

OBJECTIVES   When you have finished this section you should be able to:
- discuss the role of **oxides of nitrogen** and **hydrocarbons** in producing **ozone** and **photochemical** smog in the **lower atmosphere**;
- describe the effect of **chlorofluorocarbons (CFCs)** on the depletion of natural **ozone** in the **upper atmosphere**.

Read about the way petrochemical smog is produced and the effects of CFCs on depleting ozone either from your textbook or a scientific magazine. You should also study Fig. 20 which shows the position of the ozone shield in the upper atmosphere (stratosphere). Don't worry if you are unable to find a detailed account since we give you one in the following comprehension exercise.

The first part of the question requires you to write a summary. This type of question is becoming popular with examination boards. Check to see if you will be set this type of question in your final exam. Whether it is or not, it is a useful skill to practise. We include a few tips here to help you tackle this type of exercise.

- Write as your title the task you are asked to do in the relevant question. This will help you keep to the **relevant chemistry**. (Words in the title don't count in the word total.)
- **Identify** the **key points** either by highlighting on the question paper or listing as rough work before attempting to write your summary in **continuous prose**.
- Write on **alternate lines**, this allows any alterations to be made clearly.
- Make effective use of **relevant equations**, incorporating equations into the text, rather than presenting them separately.
- If a **rough draft** is produced, clearly cross it through to avoid any risk of this being taken by the examiner as the final version.
- Do not use **excess words**. In some cases, for every 5 words in excess of the maximum, one mark is deducted up to a maximum of 10. It is better to use at least 5 words less than maximum to allow for errors in counting or interpretation. For example, '70–80%' is counted as three words by some examiners!

EXERCISE 72

Answers on page 144

Read the passage below entitled 'Ozone – Friend or Foe?' starting overleaf, and answer the following questions based on it.

a Popular discussion of environmental issues is often limited by a lack of the relevant scientific understanding. One such topic is the damage to the ozone layer of the atmosphere by our use of such products as aerosols. Ozone also plays an important, though less well-known, role in the formation of photochemical smogs in some of the world's large cities.

Imagine that you have been asked to produce a brief paper on the relevant chemistry of ozone for the benefit of non-science A-level students who have a broad background of science.

Your paper should include what you consider to be the most important points about the chemistry of ozone **relevant to its role in the atmosphere**.

From the passage identify the key points, and use them to write your paper, as continuous prose, in **no more than 150 words**. You are **not** asked to summarise the whole passage.

Credit will be given for answers written in good English, using complete sentences and with correct use of technical words. Do not copy sentences or long phrases of the original text. Numbers count as one word, as do standard abbreviations and hyphenated words. Neither the title you give nor any chemical equations you include count in the word total.

At the end state clearly the number of words you have used.

Figure 20
Position of ozone layer in the upper stratosphere.

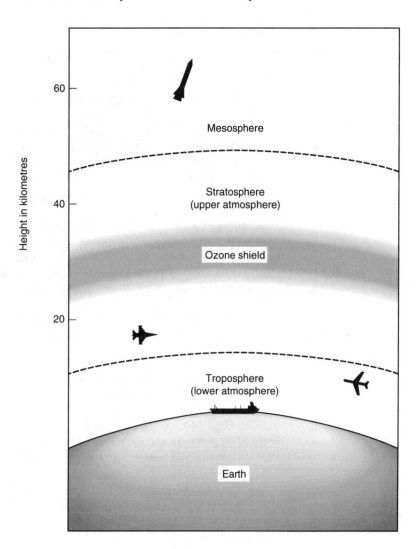

Ozone – Friend or Foe?

Ozone is in the news! Or at least the ozone layer in the upper atmosphere, whose problems have caught the headlines for the past 16 years; first an Antarctic hole, then an Arctic hole, and all due, it is said, to the use of chlorofluorocarbons (CFCs) in aerosols, refrigerators and foams.

But what is ozone, and how much do we know about it? A dictionary of chemistry calls it 'an allotrope of oxygen', states that it has a blue colour and refers to it as a 'toxic gas'. It is distinguished from oxygen by having three atoms in its molecule, rather than two as for 'ordinary' oxygen. It occurs naturally in the atmosphere at various levels, being produced by the photochemical dissociation of oxygen molecules:

$$O_2 \xrightarrow{hv} 2 \bullet O \bullet, \quad \text{followed by} \quad O_2 + \bullet O \bullet \to O_3$$

However, it is constantly removed by such processes as:

$$O_3 + \bullet O \bullet \to 2O_2 \quad \text{and} \quad NO + O_3 \to NO_2 + O_2$$

while it also has to compete for free oxygen atoms with other processes:

$$NO_2 + \bullet O \bullet \to NO + O_2$$

resulting in an equilibrium situation with a steady concentration of ozone. Its presence in the upper atmosphere is particularly important to us as it absorbs some of the harmful ultraviolet radiation from the Sun. Ozone is also present in the lower atmosphere, where it acts as a 'greenhouse' gas, like carbon dioxide, by strongly absorbing infrared radiation from the Earth beneath as well as from solar radiation. Both upper and lower ozone layers thus absorb energy and so have a major effect on the circulation of the Earth's atmosphere, which in turn affects our climate. So any changes in the concentration of ozone can have potentially damaging results.

Ozone is produced in electrical equipment, especially electric motors, where electric sparks pass through air, and this is the basis of its preparation in which an electrical discharge is passed through oxygen flowing down a tube in an apparatus called an ozoniser. The gas is very unstable:

$$2O_3 \to 3O_2; \quad \Delta H^\circ = -326 \text{ kJ mol}^{-1}$$

and at high concentrations of ozone this reaction can be explosive. Chemically, ozone is characterised by its power as an oxidising agent, being a more powerful oxidising agent than oxygen; it will, for example, oxidise iodide ions to iodine, sulphide ions to sulphate ions and ammonia to nitrate ions. Another important property is its reaction with the double bond in alkenes to form ozonides:

These ozonides may be hydrolysed with rupture of the molecule into two carbonyl compounds (aldehydes and ketones) which can be used to give us information about the location of the double bond in the alkene. The chemical reactivity of ozone finds a biological application in the purification of water supplies, making use of its ability to kill bacteria; it has several advantages over chlorine, such as lower toxicity and less effect on the taste of the water, but it is also more expensive.

The threat to the ozone layer comes not from its power as an oxidising agent, but from its ability to react with free radicals, or with molecules such as NO. One such free radical is the chlorine atom, and chlorine atoms are formed in the upper

40   atmosphere where CFC molecules are broken down by ultraviolet radiation. So the ozone equilibrium is upset by competing reactions:

$$Cl\bullet + O_3 \rightarrow ClO + O_2 \quad and \quad ClO + \bullet O\bullet \rightarrow Cl\bullet + O_2$$

    The first reaction speeds up the removal of ozone, while the second decreases its rate of formation by the removal of the free oxygen atoms, resulting in a decrease in the ozone concentration.

45   A further environmental threat involving ozone occurs lower in the atmosphere when nitrogen oxides such as NO_2 are formed during the combustion of fossil fuels. Ultraviolet radiation again causes dissociation:

$$NO_2 \xrightarrow{h\nu} NO + \bullet O\bullet$$

leading to

$$O_2 + \bullet O\bullet \longrightarrow O_3$$

    The toxicity of ozone makes it a secondary pollutant, resulting from a reaction of
50   one of the primary pollutants. In its turn it may react with NO, as it does in the upper atmosphere, to form NO_2 and O_2 again, but if unburnt hydrocarbons are present, as they are in the traffic of busy city streets, the ozone reacts with these to form unpleasant organic compounds, the whole mixture forming what is called a **photochemical smog**.

55   So what have we found? As is so often the case, there is no simple conclusion in answer to the question in our title; vital in the right place, yet harmful in the wrong place – and so many places in between where it may be anything from useful to a nuisance. But without its vital presence in one place – the upper atmosphere – we, and most other living things, would probably not have evolved on this planet; and
60   unless we learn how to control our use of the atmosphere so that we maintain that vital 'ozone layer', we may not continue to be here much longer!

763 words

  b Too much ozone in the lower atmosphere
    i) Why is too much ozone in the lower atmosphere harmful?
    ii) Until more recently the concentration of ozone in the atmosphere was more or less constant. Why was this?
    iii) Ozone episodes in which ozone concentrations rise substantially above the background levels tend to occur more frequently in summer heat waves. Why is this?
    iv) Describe with equations why increased levels of NO_2 affect ozone concentrations in the lower atmosphere.
    v) One of the compounds in photochemical smog is peroxyacetyl nitrate or PAN ($CH_3—CO—O—O—NO_2$). Which substances other than ozone and NO_2 must be present to produce it?
    vi) What is the major source responsible for the increasing concentrations of NO_2 and hydrocarbons in the atmosphere?
  c Too little ozone in the upper atmosphere
    i) Too little ozone in the upper atmosphere is harmful. Why?
    ii) Which substances have been implicated in the depletion of ozone and where do they originate?
    iii) CFCs are inert in the lower atmosphere but in the upper atmosphere they undergo photochemical decomposition to form chlorine radicals. The equations at the end of line 41 show how these free radicals affect the ozone layer. Explain why this sequence of reactions is described as a free radical chain reaction.

Clothing and hats protect these children from the sun on an Australian beach.

iv) Combine the two equations into a single equation.
v) What part are the chlorine free radicals playing in this sequence?
vi) What measures should be taken to protect the ozone layer in the upper atmosphere?

A collection of CFC-free products.

Meanwhile there is still a hole in the ozone layer above the Antarctic. Since some CFCs have an atmospheric lifetime of up to 380 years, taking a long time to diffuse upwards, concentrations of chlorine in the upper atmosphere would continue to increase even if further emissions ceased today. You will look at CFCs, their properties, uses and alternatives in the last section of this volume dealing with halogen compounds.

We now consider a method for reducing levels of hydrocarbons and oxides of nitrogen, pollutants which, as we have seen, cause an increase in ozone which in turn gives rise to photochemical smog.

■ 6.5 Controlling car exhaust emissions

OBJECTIVES   When you have finished this section you should be able to:
■ describe the pollution effects of the **internal combustion engine** and the use of **catalytic converters** to reduce them;
■ discuss the relationship between **car emissions** and **engine speeds**.

Car exhausts release carbon monoxide, hydrocarbons, oxides of nitrogen and carbon dioxide into the atmosphere; apart from carbon dioxide, it is possible to remove these gases by passing the exhaust fumes through a catalytic converter.

You may find it difficult to find information about how a catalytic converter operates from your textbooks. Your teacher may be able to provide you with details from scientific journals or magazines. If not don't worry: we have set out an account which forms part of a comprehension exercise which you should now attempt.

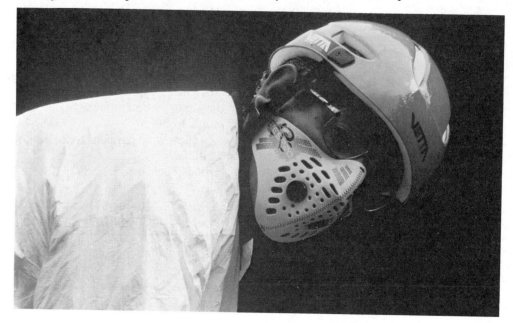

EXERCISE 73

Answers on page 146

Read the following account which describes the function of a catalytic converter and attempt the questions which follow.

Catalytic converter

In London alone, more than 1.3 million tonnes of pollutants are pumped into the atmosphere each year. It is estimated that more than 80 per cent of these come from cars. A car belches out four main pollutants which put human health or the environment at risk. They are carbon monoxide, which is poisonous to humans and contributes to the greenhouse effect; hydrocarbons, which irritate the lungs and react photochemically with sunlight to produce smog; carbon dioxide, the main greenhouse gas; and oxides of nitrogen, which combine with water in the atmosphere to produce nitric acid, a component of acid rain. These oxides also help form photochemical smog.

Catalytic converters, or 'cats', are designed to remove these pollutants. A full 'three-way' catalytic converter, now used by many car manufacturers, can remove up to 90%.

The first significant research into the use of catalytic converters was carried out in the 1950s by General Motors in the United States. The company based its work on the studies of Eugene Houdry, who had discovered that the catalytic method of breaking crude oil down into its constituent parts (petrol, paraffin, diesel and heavy engine oil) could remove dangerous elements from petrol engine exhaust gases.

A catalytic converter works through a basic chemical reaction. When the car's exhaust gases reach the converter, they pass through a honeycomb-like structure, called a cellular ceramic substrate. This is coated with a thin layer of platinum and other precious metals, and maximises the surface area over which the gases pass. The metals act as a catalyst, beginning a reaction that changes the chemical composition of the gases.

Platinum and palladium convert unburned hydrocarbons and carbon monoxide into carbon dioxide and water vapour. Rhodium converts oxides of nitrogen and hydrocarbons into nitrogen and water, which are harmless. Although 'cats' are only about 30 cm long by 23 cm wide, the substrate's total surface area is 23,000 square metres, the size of two football pitches.

Educational Guardian, page 4, 22 January 1991 (H. Birch).

a Why is the catalyst arranged over a honeycomb-like structure?

b Name the catalysts. In which block do they appear in the Periodic Table?

c Where do each of the gases, carbon monoxide, carbon dioxide, hydrocarbons and oxides of nitrogen, come from?

d Write equations which show what happens to the following gases when they pass over the Pt/Pd oxidation catalyst.
   i) Unburnt hydrocarbons, such as hexane C_6H_{14}.
   ii) Carbon monoxide.

e A three-way catalyst can remove all pollutant gases including nitrogen oxides as well, using a reduced catalyst such as rhodium. Complete the following equation to show how this might be achieved.

$$CO \text{ (g)} + NO_2 \text{ (g)} \rightarrow$$

We now look at the effect of engine speed on car exhaust emissions.

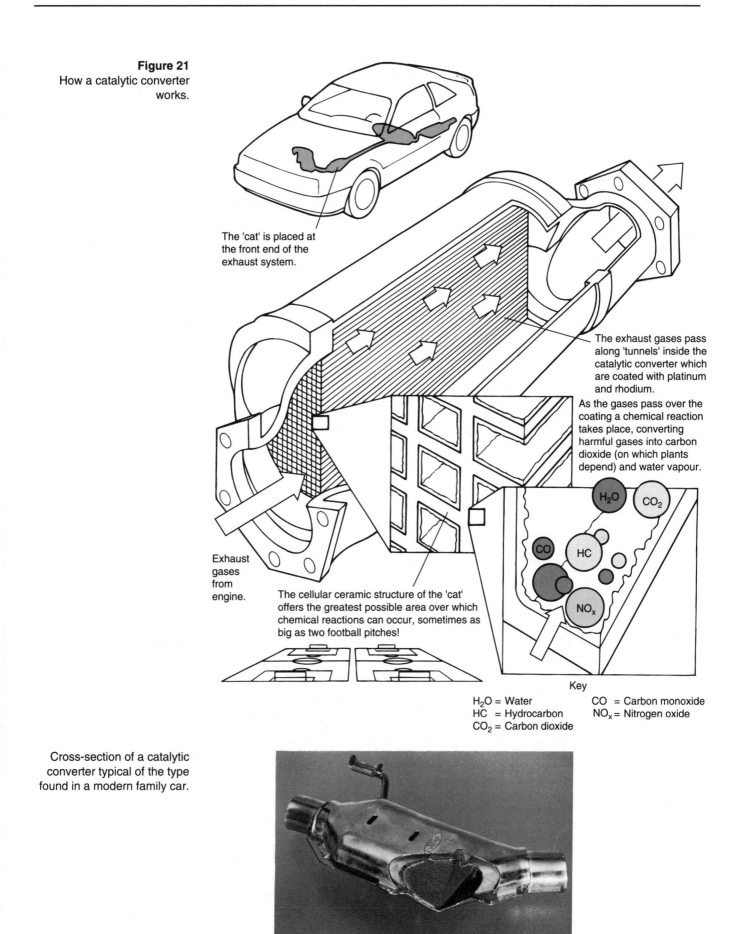

Figure 21
How a catalytic converter works.

The 'cat' is placed at the front end of the exhaust system.

The exhaust gases pass along 'tunnels' inside the catalytic converter which are coated with platinum and rhodium.

As the gases pass over the coating a chemical reaction takes place, converting harmful gases into carbon dioxide (on which plants depend) and water vapour.

Exhaust gases from engine.

The cellular ceramic structure of the 'cat' offers the greatest possible area over which chemical reactions can occur, sometimes as big as two football pitches!

Key

H_2O = Water   CO = Carbon monoxide
HC = Hydrocarbon NO_x = Nitrogen oxide
CO_2 = Carbon dioxide

Cross-section of a catalytic converter typical of the type found in a modern family car.

■ 6.6 Engine speed

We are often reminded that speed kills. The fact that speed pollutes as well is not often mentioned. The next exercise shows how pollution from vehicles varies with speed and considers the current legislation on speed limits and how it might be changed to produce less pollution.

EXERCISE 74

Answers on page 146

Figures 22–25 show how the amounts of carbon dioxide, carbon monoxide, hydrocarbons and nitrogen oxides in the exhaust vary with speed for a typical family car. Study them and attempt the questions which follow.

Figure 22
Carbon dioxide emissions of a typical car.

Figure 23
Carbon monoxide emissions of a typical car.

Figure 24
Hydrocarbon emissions of a typical car.

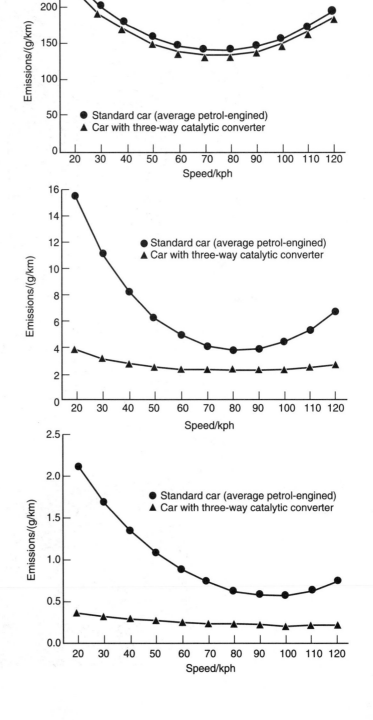

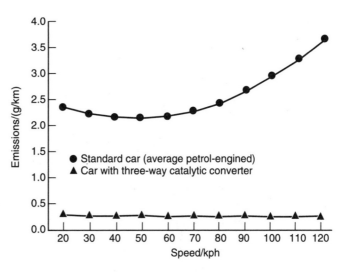

Figure 25
Nitrogen oxide emissions of a typical car.

a Find the optimal speed in mph for each pollutant gas (i.e. the speed which produces the minimum amount of pollution). (Conversion: 40 kph = 25 mph.)

b Table 19 lists the current speed limits in Britain for different types of vehicle. Study it and the information beneath it and attempt the questions which follow. (Speed limits for 1993 in mph.)

Table 19

	Single carriageway (urban)	Single carriageway (rural)	Dual carriageway	Motorway
Car	30	60	70	70
Bus	30	50	60	70
HGV	30	40	50	60

From 1 August 1992 all heavy goods vehicles (HGV) over 7.5 tonnes were fitted with governors which prevent them from breaking the 60 mph limit.

i) What measures could be taken to reduce pollutant emissions from the different vehicles, and how could they be implemented?

ii) Contrary to expectations, governors have proved popular with some road contractors. Why do you think this is?

Carbon monoxide gas is produced not only by cars but also by coal or gas fires which are not properly ventilated.

■ 6.7 Carbon monoxide

OBJECTIVE   When you have finished this section you should be able to:
■ describe the effects of **carbon monoxide poisoning** and the precautions which need to be taken to avoid it.

Read from a textbook about the effects of carbon monoxide poisoning. You may find a biology book more helpful. You should then be able to do the next exercise.

EXERCISE 75

Answers on page 146

There are many reported cases of tragic deaths due to accidental carbon monoxide poisoning.

a What causes a coal or gas fire to produce this gas?

b Why is it difficult to be aware of carbon monoxide poisoning?

c How does carbon monoxide affect the blood?

d What precautions should you take to avoid carbon monoxide poisoning?

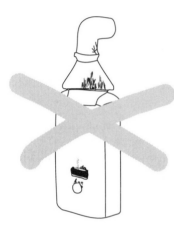

The golden rules of gas safety

Gas is a very safe fuel, but the appliances that run on gas need air to breathe – just like you and me. Follow these simple rules and enjoy your gas appliances in safety.

- **Make sure** the flue or chimney above or behind a gas heater is not blocked or damaged. If it is, poisonous fumes will leak into the room.
- **Don't** block or seal window or wall ventilators.
- **Have** all your gas appliances serviced regularly and only use British Gas or qualified CORGI contractors.
- **Never** try 'Do It Yourself' with gas.
- **Make sure** that your gas appliances are clean and free from fluff.
- **Make sure** the door or window is open while running hot water, if the water heater is in the same room.
- **Turn off** the water heater before you get in the bath.
- **Never** hang clothes over the water heater or any other gas appliance to dry.
- **Don't** remove guards from gas appliances, particularly fires.
- **Never** use a gas cooker to heat a room.

If you smell gas telephone British Gas immediately (the phone number is under gas in the telephone book). The emergency service operates 24 hours a day, all year round.

As a result of the Gas Safety (Installation and Use) Regulations 1994, landlords are now required to have all gas appliances checked once a year for safety by a qualified CORGI installer. Tenants have the right to see proof that the check has been carried out. Landlords and installers face fines, and even jail sentences if they fail to comply.

To consolidate your understanding of this section you should attempt the following Teacher-marked Exercise. Since you may also wish to discuss the use of lead additives in petrol you will need to revise the previous section as well.

EXERCISE

Teacher-marked

Many environmental problems require an understanding of their chemical basis if appropriate action is to be taken.

Select any **two** environmental issues such as air pollution or lead in petrol which you have studied. Describe in detail the chemical nature of each problem, suggest possible solutions and discuss what might happen if the problem is allowed to continue.

You have now completed the chapter on hydrocarbons and their effects on the environment. In the final chapter which follows you will study halogen compounds. Here we shall be interested in the properties of the carbon–halogen bond.

HALOGEN COMPOUNDS: CARBON–HALOGEN BONDS

This section deals with halogenoalkanes and halogenoarenes. In these compounds, the halogen atom is attached to a saturated carbon atom or to a benzene ring. Two examples are shown below.

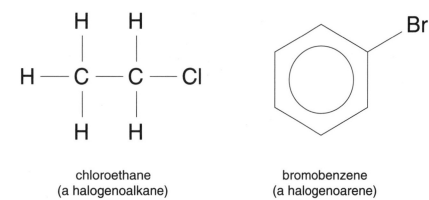

chloroethane
(a halogenoalkane)

bromobenzene
(a halogenoarene)

Alternative names for halogenoalkanes are alkyl halides and haloalkanes; alternative names for halogenoarenes are aryl halides, halobenzenes and halogenobenzenes.

■ 7.1 Names and structural formulae

Read the introductory chapter or section on halogen compounds in your textbook. If your particular textbook deals with aliphatic and aromatic compounds separately, you may have to look in two chapters. Look for the systematic names of halogenoalkanes and halogenoarenes, including halogenoarenes with more than one substituent in the ring. Also make sure you can recognise primary (1°), secondary (2°) and tertiary (3°) halogenoalkanes. You should then be able to do Exercises 76–78.

EXERCISE 76
Answers on page 146

Name the following compounds:
a $CH_3CH_2CHClCH_3$

b $(CH_3)_3CBr$

c CH_3CH_2I

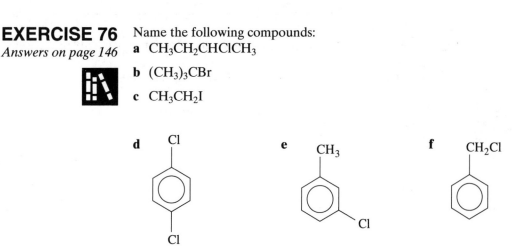

d Cl ... Cl

e CH_3 ... Cl

f CH_2Cl

EXERCISE 77

Answers on page 146

Write the structural formulae of the following compounds:

a 2-chloro-2-methylpropane,
b 3-bromopentane,
c bromobenzene,
d 1-chloro-4-methylbenzene,
e 1,3-dichlorobenzene.

EXERCISE 78

Answers on page 147

Identify the following as primary, secondary or tertiary halogenoalkanes:

a $CH_3CH_2CHBrCH_3$,
b $CH_3CH_2CH_2CH_2CH_2Br$,
c $CH_3CH_2C(CH_3)_2Br$,
d $(CH_3)_3CCl$,
e C_2H_5I.

You now investigate some of the chemical properties of these organic halogen compounds.

■ 7.2 Chemical properties of halogen compounds

OBJECTIVE

When you have finished this section you should be able to:
■ compare the **rates of hydrolysis** of some halogen compounds.

In the next exercise, you compare the strengths of the carbon–halogen bonds in some halogen compounds and make a prediction about potential reactivity.

EXERCISE 79

Answer on page 147

Table 20

Bond		Bond energy /kJ mol^{-1}
C—Cl		338
C—Br	in halogenoalkanes	276
C—I		238
C—Cl	in 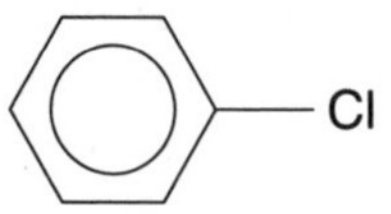 ⬡—Cl	365

Use the data listed in Table 20 to predict the likely order of reactivity of the following compounds:

1-chlorobutane, 1-bromobutane, 1-iodobutane, chlorobenzene.

 In the experiment which follows, you test your prediction by investigating the hydrolysis of halogen compounds.

EXPERIMENT 3   Hydrolysis of organic halogen compounds

Aim

The purpose of this experiment is to find out how the rate of hydrolysis of an organic halogen compound depends on:

a the identity of the halogen atom,

b the nature of the carbon–hydrogen 'skeleton'.

Introduction

In this experiment, you compare the rates of hydrolysis of 1-chlorobutane, 1-bromobutane, 1-iodobutane and chlorobenzene. A general equation for the hydrolysis is:

$$R—X + H_2O \rightarrow R—OH + H^+ + X^-$$

(where R = alkyl or aryl group; X = halogen atom).

You can follow the rate of the reaction by carrying it out in the presence of silver ions, so that any halide ions produced form a silver halide precipitate.

$$Ag^+ (aq) + X^- (aq) \rightarrow AgX (s)$$

Since halogenoalkanes and halogenoarenes are insoluble in water, ethanol is added to act as a common solvent for the halogeno-compounds and silver ions.

Requirements

- safety spectacles
- Bunsen burner, tripod, gauze and bench protection sheet (or a theromostatically controlled water-bath, set at 60°C)
- beaker, 250 cm^3
- thermometer, 0–100°C
- 5 test-tubes fitted with corks
- test-tube rack
- waterproof marker or chinagraph pencil
- protective plastic gloves
- measuring cylinder, 10 cm^3
- ethanol, C_2H_5OH
- 1-chlorobutane, C_4H_9Cl
- 1-bromobutane, C_4H_9Br
- 1-iodobutane, C_4H_9I
- chlorobenzene, C_6H_5Cl
- silver nitrate solution, 0.05 M $AgNO_3$
- stop-clock (or clock with seconds hand)

HAZARD WARNING

All organic halogen compounds have harmful vapours and can be toxic by absorption through the skin. Some are flammable. Therefore you **must**:

- **keep the stoppers on the bottles as much as possible;**
- **keep the bottles away from flames;**
- **wear safety spectacles and gloves.**

Procedure   1. Set up the apparatus shown in Fig. 26 (or switch on your electric water-bath). Make sure none of the test-tubes contains any tap-water; this would give an immediate precipitate with silver nitrate and spoil your results.

Figure 26

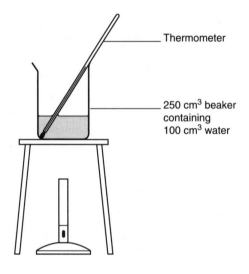

2. Pour 2 cm^3 of ethanol into each of four test-tubes and mark them with the letters A to D.
3. Add 3–4 drops of 1-chlorobutane to A, 3–4 drops of 1-bromobutane to B, 3–4 drops of 1-iodobutane to C and 3–4 drops of chlorobenzene to D.
4. Pour about 5 cm^3 of silver nitrate solution into the fifth test-tube.
5. Stand all the test-tubes in the beaker (or water-bath) and heat to 60°C. Remove the Bunsen burner.
6. Quickly add 1 cm^3 of aqueous silver nitrate to each of the tubes A to D and start the stop-clock. Shake each tube once to mix the contents, and leave in the water with the cork resting **loosely** on the tube to reduce evaporation.
7. Watch the tubes continuously for about ten minutes and note, in a copy of Results Table 4, the time when a precipitate first appears in each tube as a definite cloudiness. If necessary, heat the water to 60°C again at intervals.
8. Continue observation at intervals for about 30 minutes more, noting any further changes in the appearance of the precipitates.

Results Table 4

Reaction	Time for precipitate to appear	Observations
A 1-Chlorobutane		
B 1-Bromobutane		
C 1-Iodobutane		
D Chlorobenzene		

(Specimen results on page 147.)

Questions

Answers on page 147

1. List the compounds in order of speed of hydrolysis, fastest first.
2. Was the prediction you made in Exercise 79 verified by experiment?
3. Write equations for the hydrolysis reactions which take place in this experiment.

In the next exercise you consider some implications of the work you have just done.

EXERCISE 80

Answers on page 147

a Suggest a reason why iodoalkanes are often used in organic chemistry in preference to the corresponding bromine or chlorine compounds.
b 'Non-stick' frying pans are coated with an organic fluoro-compound, PTFE (polytetrafluoroethene). Why is there little risk of food contamination by the fluorine?

In the next exercise you look at the structure of chlorobenzene to explain the apparent inertness of the substance.

EXERCISE 81

Answer on page 147

It is believed that, in chlorobenzene, lone-pair electrons of the chlorine atom become involved in the π-electron system of the benzene ring. Figure 27(a) shows the individual p-orbitals; Fig. 27(b) shows how the p-electrons form the π-electron system in the ring.

Figure 27(a)

Figure 27(b)

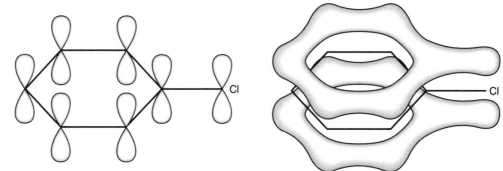

How does this help to explain the apparent inertness of chlorobenzene to hydrolysis?

You now know how the reactivity of an organic halogen compound with respect to hydrolysis depends on the identity of the halogen atom and the nature of the carbon–hydrogen 'skeleton'. With this in mind attempt the next exercise.

EXERCISE 82

Answers on page 148

For each of the following pairs of compounds, give one simple chemical test that would distinguish between them. For each compound, describe exactly what you would observe (if anything) and explain the reactions which have occurred.

a

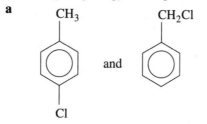

b $CH_3CH_2CH_2I$ and $CH_3CH_2CH_2Cl$

Most reactions of halogen compounds can be described as either substitution or elimination reactions. We shall consider the substitution reactions first.

■ 7.3 Substitution reactions

OBJECTIVES

When you have finished this section you should be able to:
- explain the term **nucleophilic substitution**;
- write equations for nucleophilic substitution reactions of halogenoalkanes;
- describe a **mechanism for a nucleophilic substitution** reaction of a halogenoalkane.

 Read about nucleophilic substitution reactions of halogenoalkanes and halogenoarenes in your textbook(s). Make sure you understand what is meant by the term **nucleophile**. You should then be able to do Exercises 83–85.

EXERCISE 83

Answers on page 148

a The characteristic reactions of halogenoalkanes (alkyl halides) may be described as nucleophilic substitution. Explain briefly the meaning of this term.
b What features of the molecules of halogenoalkanes make these substances susceptible to reactions of this type?

As you have seen, it is the stability of the leaving halide ion and the polar nature of the carbon–halogen bond in the halogenoalkanes which make these compounds susceptible to nucleophilic substitution reactions of the type:

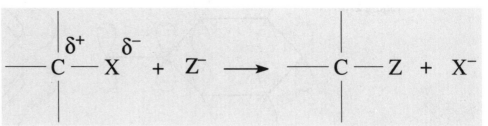

(X represents a halogen atom and Z a nucleophile which has a lone pair of electrons and may or may not be negatively charged.) With this in mind, attempt the next exercise.

EXERCISE 84

Answers on page 148

a Write equations, naming products and stating conditions, for the substitution reactions which take place between 1-bromobutane, C_4H_9Br, and the following nucleophiles:
i) OH^-,
ii) CN^-,
iii) $CH_3CO_2{}^-$,
iv) $C_2H_5O^-$,
v) H_2O,
vi) NH_3.
Mention should be made of the reagents which are required to produce some of these nucleophiles.
b Explain how the addition of aqueous sodium hydroxide solution increases the yield of ethanol in the reaction:

$$C_2H_5Cl + H_2O \rightarrow C_2H_5OH + HCl$$

In the next exercise, you consider the conditions necessary for halogenoarenes to undergo nucleophilic substitution reactions.

EXERCISE 85

Answers on page 149

Write equations for the reactions which take place between chlorobenzene and the following nucleophiles:

a OH⁻,

b NH₃.

Include details of conditions and the names of the products.

As you might have expected from the structure of chlorobenzene (Fig. 27(b), page 91) halogenoarenes are less reactive than halogenoalkanes in their reactions with nucleophiles. But, as you learned in Exercise 85, some nucleophilic substitution reactions may be carried out under extreme conditions.

Similar considerations apply to some halogenoalkenes, as you show in the next exercise.

EXERCISE 86

Answers on page 149

Account for the fact that chloroethene, CH_2=CHCl (vinyl chloride), unlike chloroethane, CH_3CH_2Cl, does not react readily with nucleophilic reagents; e.g. it is not hydrolysed by sodium hydroxide solution.

We now briefly consider the mechanism of nucleophilic substitution.

■ 7.4 The mechanism of nucleophilic substitution

Essentially, as the nucleophile moves toward the carbon atom (which carries a partial positive charge), the halogen atom breaks away to form an ion. As one bond forms, the other breaks. This is illustrated for nucleophilic substitution of a primary halogenoalkane in Fig. 28, where Z:⁻ represents the nucleophile and X the halogen atom. (Z carries a lone pair of electrons.)

Figure 28

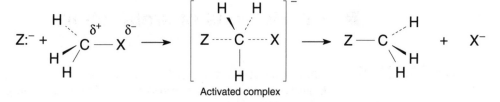

Activated complex

If the nucleophile is unchanged it is best represented as HX: (e.g. HOH, HNH₂): a proton is lost as Z forms the activated complex. Nucleophilic substitution of tertiary halogenoalkanes takes place by another mechanism involving two steps which we study in ILPAC Volume 9, Chemical Kinetics.

Now attempt the following exercise using Fig. 28 above to help you.

EXERCISE 87

Answers on page 149

Discuss the mechanism by which 1-bromopropane reacts with warm aqueous sodium hydroxide.

The reactions of halogenoalkanes with nucleophiles are complicated by the fact that an elimination reaction can take place at the same time.

■ 7.5 Elimination reactions

In these elimination reactions, a molecule of hydrogen halide is eliminated from one molecule of halogenoalkane to give an alkene.

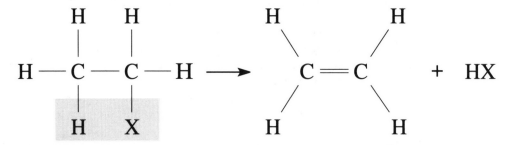

When you have finished this section you should be able to:
■ write equations for **elimination reactions of halogenoalkanes**.

Read about the elimination reactions of halogenoalkanes in your textbook(s). Find out the conditions which favour an elimination reaction rather than a substitution reaction.

EXERCISE 88
Answers on page 149

a Write the formula of the active species in a solution of hot concentrated potassium hydroxide in ethanol.
b Write a balanced equation for the elimination reaction between 2-iodopropane and ethanolic potassium hydroxide. Name the products.

Now we consider some methods of preparing halogen compounds.

■ 7.6 Methods of preparation

OBJECTIVES When you have finished this section you should be able to:
■ write equations for the **preparation of halogen compounds**, giving specific reaction conditions;
■ describe the techniques of **reflux, distillation, and use of a separating funnel;**
■ design an experiment using the techniques from the objective above and calculate **percentage yields.**

Look up the methods of preparing halogenoalkanes and halogenoarenes in your textbook(s) and then attempt the following exercise listing some of the reactions in which halogeno-compounds are produced. We make no distinction between methods which produce good or poor yields, although this is obviously important if you are deciding on a method to prepare a particular compound. You have already met some of the methods as reactions of hydrocarbons earlier in this volume. Other methods will be new; you will, however, meet them again as reactions of alcohols later in ILPAC Volume 8.

EXERCISE 89
Answers on page 150

Complete a larger copy of Table 21, which summarises the more important methods of preparing halogenoalkanes and halogenoarenes. Complete the equations given as examples and name the reactants and products. Also state any special conditions and any notes which you think are important.

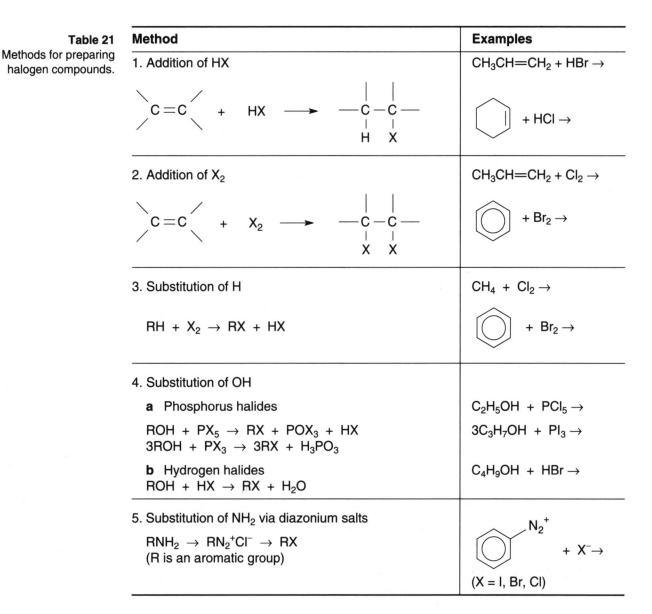

Table 21 Methods for preparing halogen compounds.

Method	Examples
1. Addition of HX	$CH_3CH=CH_2 + HBr \rightarrow$
2. Addition of X_2	$CH_3CH=CH_2 + Cl_2 \rightarrow$
3. Substitution of H $RH + X_2 \rightarrow RX + HX$	$CH_4 + Cl_2 \rightarrow$
4. Substitution of OH **a** Phosphorus halides $ROH + PX_5 \rightarrow RX + POX_3 + HX$ $3ROH + PX_3 \rightarrow 3RX + H_3PO_3$ **b** Hydrogen halides $ROH + HX \rightarrow RX + H_2O$	$C_2H_5OH + PCl_5 \rightarrow$ $3C_3H_7OH + PI_3 \rightarrow$ $C_4H_9OH + HBr \rightarrow$
5. Substitution of NH_2 via diazonium salts $RNH_2 \rightarrow RN_2^+Cl^- \rightarrow RX$ (R is an aromatic group)	$+ X^- \rightarrow$ (X = I, Br, Cl)

You will use one of these methods in the experiment which follows, but before you start it we show you how to work out a percentage yield.

■ 7.7 Working out a percentage yield

Organic preparations rarely give 100% yield. It is not uncommon for yields to be around 60% or less. This is due to the occurrence of other reactions giving different products, to reversible reactions leading to equilibrium, and to the losses that are involved in the separations. This means you rarely obtain the amount of product you would calculate from the equation. In the Worked Example which follows we show you how to work out the yield of a product from given quantities of reactants and products.

The percentage yield is given by the following expression:

$$\% \text{ yield} = \frac{\text{actual mass of product}}{\text{maximum mass of product}} \times 100$$

WORKED EXAMPLE   A student hydrolysed 10 g of 1-bromobutane and obtained 3.9 g of butan-1-ol.

$$C_4H_9Br \ + \ NaOH \ \rightarrow \ C_4H_9OH \ + \ NaBr$$
$$\text{1-bromobutane} \qquad\qquad \text{butan-1-ol}$$

Calculate the % yield of butan-1-ol.

Solution   We know the actual mass of product obtained was 3.9 g and we now need to work out the maximum mass of product which would have been obtained if all the 1-bromobutane had been converted into butan-1-ol.

1. Calculate the amount of reactant (i.e. 1-bromobutane) actually used by means of the expression

$$n = \frac{m}{M}; \quad n = \frac{10 \text{ g}}{137 \text{ g mol}^{-1}} = \mathbf{0.073 \ mol}$$

2. The equation tells you that 1 mol of 1-bromobutane produces 1 mol of butan-1-ol. We should therefore expect to produce 0.073 mol of butan-1-ol from 0.073 mol of 1-bromobutane.

3. Calculate the maximum mass of product, i.e. butan-1-ol, from the amount using

$$n = nM = 0.073 \text{ mol} \times 74 \text{ g mol}^{-1} = \mathbf{5.4 \ g}$$

4. Substitute into the expression

$$\% \text{ yield} = \frac{\text{actual mass of product}}{\text{maximum mass of product}} \times 100$$

$$= \frac{3.9 \text{ g}}{5.4 \text{ g}} \times 100 = \mathbf{72\%}$$

(yields are usually given to the nearest whole number).

You should now be able to do the next exercise. Since you usually measure out volumes of liquids rather than weigh them, the first part of the exercise requires you to convert a volume into mass.

EXERCISE 90   In an experiment, 5.1 g of iodoethane was prepared by refluxing 5.0 cm^3 of ethanol with
Answer on page 151   red phosphorus and iodine.

$$C_2H_5OH \xrightarrow[\text{heat}]{\text{P, I}_2} C_2H_5I$$
$$\text{ethanol} \qquad\qquad \text{iodoethane}$$

What was the percentage yield of the reaction? (Density of ethanol = 0.79 g cm^{-3}.)

In a synthesis with several steps, if they all have poor yields, the product may effectively disappear before the synthesis is complete.
Consider the following three-step synthesis:

$$A \xrightarrow{40\%} B \xrightarrow{40\%} C \xrightarrow{40\%} D$$
$$\text{1 mol} \qquad \text{0.4 mol} \qquad \text{0.16 mol} \qquad \text{0.064 mol}$$

If each step had a 40% yield,

$$\text{the overall yield} = \frac{40}{100} \times \frac{40}{100} \times 40\% = 6.4\%,$$

a very poor yield. This is one reason why preparations are chosen with as few steps as possible. Not only do multistage procedures produce very low yields but they also require separation at each step.

You now carry out a one-step synthesis of a halogenoalkane and have the opportunity of estimating its percentage yield.

If it is available, you will find it useful to watch the ILPAC video programme 'Organic Techniques 1' before you start the experiment. The techniques relevant to this experiment are simple distillation and the use of a separating funnel, but you will need the others later. The video programme also gives advice on the use of apparatus with ground-glass joints.

If the video programme is not available, you must ask your teacher for help in setting up the apparatus, not least because it is expensive and easily broken.

EXPERIMENT 4 Preparation of a halogenoalkane

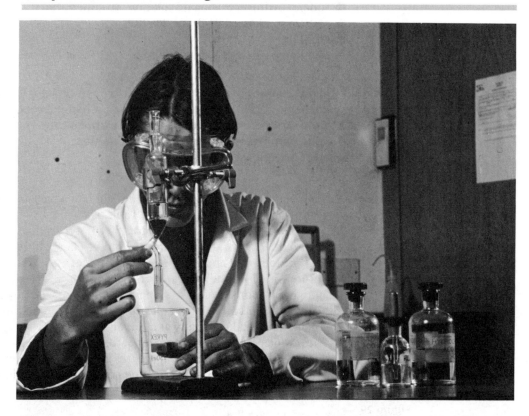

Aim The purpose of this experiment is to prepare 2-chloro-2-methylpropane and to illustrate several practical techniques employed in organic chemistry.

Introduction In this experiment you prepare 2-chloro-2-methylpropane from 2-methylpropan-2-ol and hydrochloric acid. The reaction takes place at room temperature because tertiary alcohols undergo substitution very readily.

$$CH_3 - \underset{\underset{\displaystyle OH}{|}}{\overset{\overset{\displaystyle CH_3}{|}}{C}} - CH_3 \ + \ HCl \ \longrightarrow \ CH_3 - \underset{\underset{\displaystyle Cl}{|}}{\overset{\overset{\displaystyle CH_3}{|}}{C}} - CH_3 \ + \ H_2O$$

2-methylpropan-2-ol   2-chloro-2-methylpropane

In this preparation you will meet the techniques of simple distillation and use of a separating funnel, which are commonly used in the purification of an organic liquid to give the best possible yield.

Requirements
- safety spectacles and gloves
- measuring cylinder, 25 cm^3
- 2-methylpropan-2-ol, $(CH_3)_3COH$
- access to balance, sensitivity $\pm$ 0.1 g or better
- separating funnel, 50 cm^3, with stopper
- 3 retort stands, bosses and clamps
- hydrochloric acid, concentrated, HCl
- ground-glass joint apparatus shown in Fig. 29 (with rubber tubing)
- Bunsen burner, tripod and gauze
- thermometer, 0–100°C
- conical flask, 100 cm^3, with bung
- sodium hydrogencarbonate solution, saturated, $NaHCO_3$
- sodium sulphate, anhydrous, Na_2SO_4
- spatula
- anti-bumping chips

HAZARD WARNING

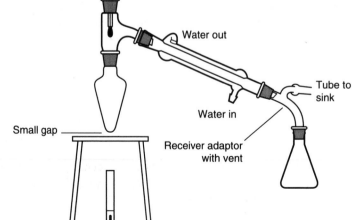

2-Chloro-2-methylpropane and 2-methylpropan-2-ol are flammable. Concentrated hydrochloric acid is corrosive and gives off a harmful vapour. Therefore you **must**:
- **keep stoppers on bottles as much as possible;**
- **keep flammable liquids away from flames;**
- **wear gloves and safety spectacles.**

Procedure
1. Pour about 9 cm^3 of 2-methylpropan-2-ol into a measuring cylinder, weigh it, and note its mass in a copy of Results Table 5.
2. Pour the 2-methylpropan-2-ol into a 50 cm^3 separating funnel and again weigh and record the mass of the measuring cylinder. Then add 20 cm^3 of concentrated hydrochloric acid about 3 cm^3 at a time. After each addition hold the stopper and tap securely in place and invert the funnel a few times; then, with the funnel in the upright position, loosen the stopper briefly to release any pressure.
3. Leave the separating funnel plus contents in the fume cupboard for about twenty minutes and shake it gently at intervals.
4. Meanwhile, set up, in a fume cupboard, a clean distillation apparatus, as shown in Fig. 29. Remember that the apparatus is a rigid assembly; you must be very careful when you clamp it at more than one point, to avoid strain and possible breakage.

Figure 29
Distillation.

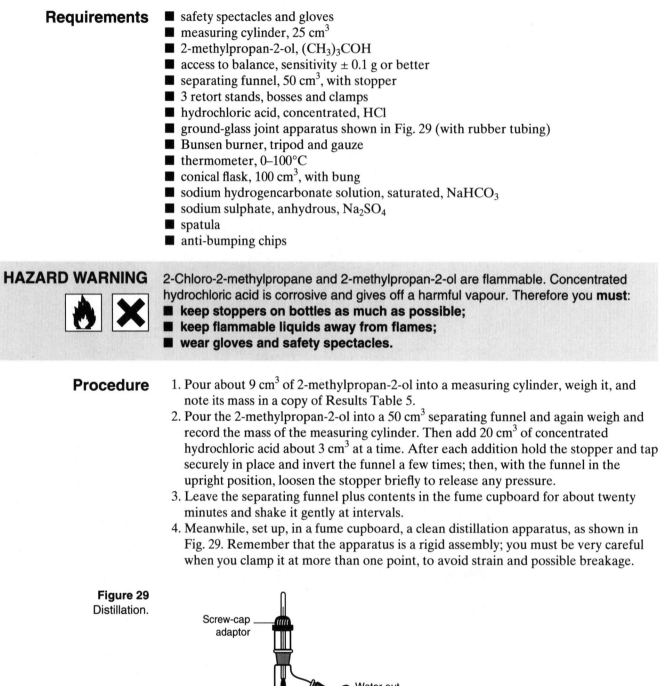

5. Weigh the small flask used as a receiver for the distillate.
6. Allow the layers in the separating funnel to separate; run off and discard the lower aqueous layer.
7. Add sodium hydrogencarbonate solution 2 cm^3 at a time in order to neutralise any excess hydrochloric acid. Shake the funnel carefully after each addition and release the pressure of carbon dioxide frequently by loosening the stopper. Continue until no more carbon dioxide is produced.
8. Allow the layers to separate; run off and discard the lower aqueous layer.
9. Run the organic layer into a small, dry conical flask and add about three spatula-measures of anhydrous sodium sulphate to dry the organic liquid. Cork and swirl the flask occasionally for about five minutes.
10. Carefully decant (pour off) the dried organic liquid from the solid sodium sulphate into the pear-shaped flask set up for distillation, as in Fig. 29. If you decant slowly, you should be able to separate the solid and liquid completely – no solid must enter the distilling flask.
11. Add a few anti-bumping granules to the pear-shaped flask and distil the 2-chloro-2-methylpropane, collecting the fraction in the range 47–53°C into the pre-weighed conical flask. Heat gently at first and then more strongly but only just strongly enough to keep the product distilling at about 1–2 drops per second.
12. Determine the mass of 2-chloro-2-methylpropane collected.

Results Table 5	
Mass of measuring cylinder + 2-methylpropan-2-ol	g
Mass of measuring cylinder after emptying	g
Mass of 2-methylpropan-2-ol	g
Mass of collecting flask	g
Mass of collecting flask + 2-chloro-2-methylpropane	g
Mass of 2-chloro-2-methylpropane	g

(Specimen results on page 151.)

Questions
Answers on page 151

1. From the chemical equation, calculate the maximum mass of 2-chloro-2-methylpropane that could be formed from the mass of 2-methylpropan-2-ol you used.
2. Calculate the percentage yield of 2-chloro-2-methylpropane using the expression

$$\% \text{ yield} = \frac{\text{actual mass of product}}{\text{maximum mass of product}} \times 100$$

3. Why is sodium hydrogencarbonate used to remove acid impurities, rather than a stronger alkali such as sodium hydroxide?

In the next Teacher-marked Exercise you will be required to design an experiment to prepare a certain amount of product assuming a given yield. You are expected to estimate suitable quantities of reagents. This is really the reverse of our previous Worked Example on page 96. We now show you how this is done.

WORKED EXAMPLE

A student is asked to prepare 6.0 g of butan-1-ol assuming a yield of 70% and is required to estimate suitable quantities of reagents.

$$C_4H_9Br + NaOH \rightarrow C_4H_9OH + NaBr$$

(Density of 1-bromobutane = 1.28 g cm^{-3}.)

Solution

1. Calculate the amount of product to be obtained by substituting into the expression:

$$n = \frac{m}{M} = \frac{6.0 \text{ g}}{74 \text{ g mol}^{-1}} = \textbf{0.081 mol}$$

2. From the equation, 1 mol of butan-1-ol is produced from 1 mol of 1-bromobutane, so amount of reactant required (i.e. 1-bromobutane) assuming a 100% yield = 0.081 mol.

3. Calculate the amount of reactant needed for the given percentage yield. For a 60% yield we should need more reagents to compensate for the loss. So amount of 1-bromobutane required

$$= \frac{100}{60} \times 0.081 \text{ mol} = \textbf{0.135 mol}$$

4. Convert amount to mass using $m = nM = 0.135 \text{ mol} \times 137 \text{ g mol}^{-1} = \textbf{18.5 g}$.

5. For liquids convert mass to volume using the expression:

$$\text{density} = \frac{\text{mass}}{\text{volume}}$$

So

$$\text{volume of 1-bromobutane} = \frac{18.5 \text{ g}}{1.28 \text{ g cm}^{-3}} = \textbf{14.5 cm}^3 \textbf{ 1-bromobutane}$$

6. Calculate the amounts of other reagents, i.e. NaOH. From the equation we should also expect to need 0.135 mol NaOH.

7. Convert amounts to mass using $m = nM = 0.135 \text{ mol} \times 40 \text{ g mol}^{-1} = 5.4 \text{ g}$ **sodium hydroxide**. This represents the minimum amount of sodium hydroxide we should use but in practice we use more than this, say 50% more, to ensure complete conversion of 1-bromobutane. You should now be able to do the next exercise.

EXERCISE 91

Answers on page 151

2-Chloro-2-methylpropane can be obtained in a yield of 62% by the following reaction

2-methylpropan-2-ol   2-chloro-2-methylpropane

Calculate suitable quantities of all reagents to prepare 5.5 g of pure 2-chloro-2-methylpropane using this method.

Density of hydrochloric acid (32% acid in water) = 1.16 g cm^{-3}
Density of 2-methylpropan-2-ol = 0.79 g cm^{-3}

You should now be ready to use this method to help you plan the preparation of another halogenoalkane.

In Experiment 4, the reaction between 2-methylpropan-2-ol and concentrated hydrochloric acid took place readily at room temperature. The preparation of other halogenoalkanes may need more drastic conditions; for instance, in the preparation of 1-bromobutane. In the next section you will design an experiment to prepare this compound.

■ 7.8 Designing an experiment – preparation of 1-bromobutane

As part of your practical coursework you may be required to design an experiment. Even if you are not, some examination questions may ask you to write instructions on a particular experiment for a fellow student to follow. We set such a task in the following Teacher-marked Exercise.

If it is available, you will find it useful to watch the ILPAC video programme 'Organic Techniques 1' in the sections dealing with reflux and distillation. If it's not available you should read about the techniques of reflux, distillation and purification in your organic textbook.

EXERCISE
Teacher-marked

Internal assessment: planning and design
Butan-1-ol reacts with hydrogen bromide to form 1-bromobutane:

$$C_4H_9OH + HBr \rightarrow C_4H_9Br + H_2O$$

The hydrogen bromide is conveniently prepared *in situ* by the reaction of potassium bromide and moderately concentrated sulphuric acid. At temperatures much below 100°C it is difficult to obtain an acceptable yield in a reasonable length of time.

You should design an experiment to prepare a **pure** sample of about 5 g of 1-bromobutane (assume a yield of 70%).

Your written account should include details of:
i)   suitable quantities of reagents;
ii) the apparatus you would use at each stage;
iii) experimental techniques;
iv) hazards and safety precautions.

You will find the information in Table 22 useful.

Table 22

Liquid	Density/g cm^{-3}	Boiling point/°C
Butan-1-ol	0.8	117
Water	1.0	100
1-Bromobutane	1.3	102
Moderately concentrated sulphuric acid	1.4	100

You may also use any other relevant information from your data book. You will not be asked to carry out this experiment.

You now summarise the reactions and methods of preparation of halogenoalkanes and halogenoarenes.

■ 7.9 Summary of reactions and preparations

EXERCISE 92
Answers on page 152

Complete copies of Figs 30 and 31 to summarise the preparations and reactions of halogenoalkanes and halogenoarenes. Use the usual format

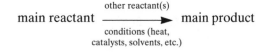

Figure 30
Summary of
preparations and
properties of
1-bromopropane.

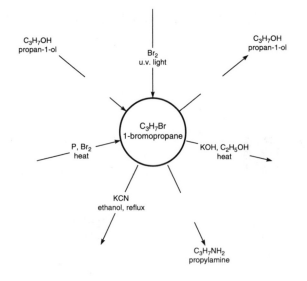

Figure 31
Summary of
preparations and
properties of
bromobenzene.

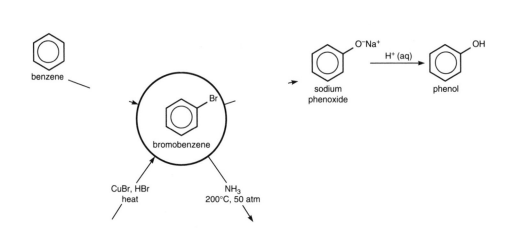

Now that you have learned the reactions of several functional groups, you can begin to
link them together to form what we shall call 'synthetic pathways'.

■ 7.10 Synthetic pathways

Industrial chemists and research chemists spend a good deal of time in working out ways
of making particular compounds from readily available materials. In organic chemistry
particularly, there may be many steps involved in such a synthetic pathway:

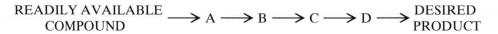

A, B, C and D in the scheme above may have their own particular uses, or they may
simply be intermediates which are converted completely in the next step.

In your study of synthetic pathways, you will not often cover the complete process from raw material (petroleum, coal, plant or animal materials) to commercial product. However, the pathways you do study usually form **parts** of such syntheses, either in industry or in research, or resemble them very closely.

Working out synthetic pathways not only helps you to learn the basic reactions of the various functional groups, but also gives you some insight into the way chemists use their knowledge to solve problems.

Unless stated otherwise the synthetic pathways which appear in examination questions expect you to use the basic laboratory reactions (general methods) in order to produce the desired product. However you should appreciate that in the actual commercial manufacture of a product the capital cost of the plant as well as the cost of the raw materials may well mean that it is preferable to use different conditions for large-scale manufacture. For example it will usually be sensible to carry out oxidation using air or oxygen and reduction using hydrogen, both aided by suitable catalysts at appropriate temperatures, rather than with expensive laboratory reagents.

In line with A-level syllabuses we only expect you to use the basic laboratory methods of synthesis (unless stated otherwise) even if it might be impracticable on a large scale.

In the following Worked Example, we give you some guidance in solving a simple problem in synthesis.

WORKED EXAMPLE   Show how you would bring about the following conversion in no more than three steps.

$$CH_3CH_2CH_2Br \rightarrow CH_3CHBrCH_2Br$$

Solution   1. List the compounds which you know can be made directly from the given starting material. To begin with, limit your list to those compounds with the same number of carbon atoms as the starting material and/or the final product.

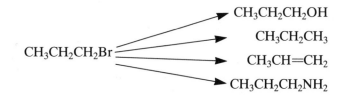

2. Alongside the list from step 1 list the compounds which you know can be converted into the final product. Again, limit your list, in the first instance, to compounds with the same number of carbon atoms as the starting material and/or the final product.

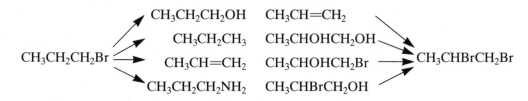

3. Find a link between the two lists. If you are lucky, the same compound may appear in both lists; if not, you must think of a method for converting **one** member of the first list to **one** member of the second. In this example $CH_3CH=CH_2$ appears in both lists, so you can write the complete pathway, inserting reaction conditions in the usual way.

$$CH_3CH_2CH_2Br \xrightarrow[\text{heat}]{\text{ethanolic KOH}} CH_3CH=CH_2 \xrightarrow[\text{inert solvent}]{Br_2} CH_3CHBrCH_2Br$$

As you gain more experience you will find that you can work out the steps for a synthetic pathway in your head but, if you get stuck, writing lists should be helpful.

The synthetic pathways in the next exercise, or very similar ones, have all appeared in examination questions.

EXERCISE 93

Answers on page 153

Show how you could bring about the following conversions. Indicate reagents, conditions and intermediate products.

a $CH_3CH_2CH_2Cl \rightarrow CH_3CH_2CH_2Br$

b

| CH₃ | → | CH₂CN |

c

| CH₂CH₂Cl | → | CHClCH₃ |

d $CH_3CHBrCH_3 \rightarrow CH_3CHBrCH_2Br$

e

| CH=CH₂ | → | CHNH₂CH₂NH₂ |

You have seen that halogeno-compounds are very useful in synthetic pathways, and this makes them very important in industry and research. Some halogeno-compounds have properties which make them important commercial products in their own right.

■ 7.11 Uses of halogeno-compounds

Although A-level students are rarely examined in any detail on this aspect of organic chemistry, we think that you should have some background information which links your study with everyday life. Too many chemistry students are ill-equipped to discuss the impact of chemistry on society.

OBJECTIVES

When you have finished this section you should be able to:
■ describe the **commercial uses** of some **halogeno-compounds**;
■ describe the **properties of CFCs** which make them a hazard to the environment and the problems of finding safe alternatives.

Read about the uses of halogeno-compounds, including fluoro-compounds, in your textbook(s). Look for references to solvents, insecticides, aerosol propellants, refrigerants, anaesthetics and fire-extinguishers. You should then be able to do the following exercise. You should also look out for possible safe alternatives to CFCs (your teacher may suggest some recent articles).

EXERCISE 94

Answers on page 153

a State the name and formula of a compound (other than DDT) which is of prime importance in the control of locusts.

b Why is the use of DDT as an insecticide now restricted?

c What properties of CFCs (chlorofluoro derivatives of hydrocarbons such as methane and ethane) have made them useful as refrigerants, aerosol propellants and fire-extinguishers?

d Why are chemists now searching for alternatives to CFCs?

e Name a compound which has replaced tetrachloromethane ('carbon tet') and 1,1,1-trichloroethane as a dry-cleaning liquid.

f Trichloromethane (chloroform) was once widely used as an anaesthetic. A similar, but safer, compound has taken its place in some applications; what is it?

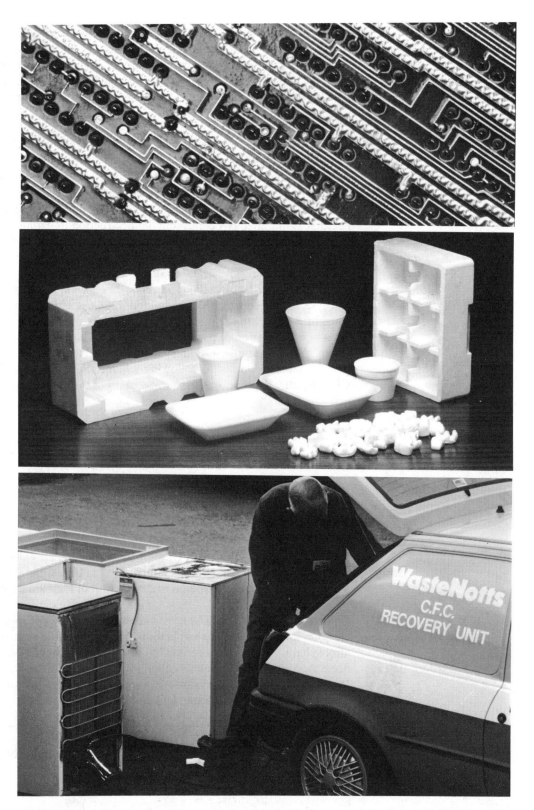

The ozone layer tolerates very little added chlorine, as you learnt earlier in Exercise 72. Solvents such as 1,1,1-trichloroethane and CFC 113 (trichlorotrifluoroethane) are widely used to remove grease, dust and even fingerprints from metal engine parts and printed circuitboards. These solvents are estimated to contribute to about 30% of the chlorine in the stratosphere. In June 1990, the Montreal Protocol set the year 2000 to phase out CFCs and tetrachloromethane and the year 2005 for 1,1,1-trichloroethane.

It is estimated that 30 000 tonnes of CFC-refrigerants are locked up in old fridges. This could be released if not disposed of with care. Friends of the Earth is pressing local councils to dispose of CFCs from domestic fridges safely. They are also pressing for legislation to make the dumping of fridges illegal. The chemicals industry is trying to develop alternatives to CFCs that do the same job but don't have the drawbacks.

■ 7.12 CFCs – a search for safe alternatives

As we have already seen in an earlier section, the problem with CFCs is their inertness in the lower atmosphere which allows them to eventually find their way into the upper atmosphere. Once there, they undergo photochemical decomposition to form free radicals, simultaneously catalysing the destruction of ozone.

The challenge for research chemists was to develop alternative compounds which did the job as well but posed no danger to the individual or the environment. The answer was to substitute all or some of the chlorine atoms in CFCs for hydrogen. By reducing or even eliminating chlorine from the molecules, there is less or no environmental problem with chlorine. For those which still contained some chlorine, the hydrogen would introduce some instability into the molecule, enabling it to break down in the lower atmosphere. So, a new generation of partially halogenated CFCs was developed called HCFAs (hydrochlorofluoroalkanes) and HFAs (hydrofluoroalkanes). They are all halogenoalkanes but as the following scheme shows the new alternatives differ from CFCs by effectively substituting some or all of the chlorine for hydrogen atoms.

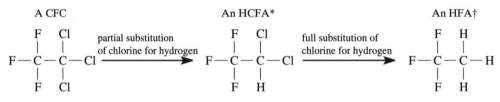

Trichlorotrifluoroethane, CFC 113
(To be phased out as a dry-cleaning fluid.)

With this in mind, you should attempt the next exercise which will give you an idea of the problems involved in finding alternatives to CFCs. You should first study Fig. 32 which shows the stages involved in destruction of the ozone layer by CFCs.

EXERCISE 95

Answers on page 154

Chlorofluorocarbons (CFCs) have been widely used as propellants, blowing agents and cleaning solvents, but their use is thought to have led to environmental damage in the atmosphere. As a result, alternative compounds are being sought. Some alkanes have been used; other replacements called HFAs (hydrofluoroalkanes) and HCFAs (hydrochlorofluoroalkanes) are being developed. Here are some data for three compounds: a CFC, an alkane, and an HCFA.

Table 23

Compound	Formula	Boiling point /K	Flammability	ODP	Price /£ kg^{-1}
A	$CFCl_3$	297	no	1.0	1000
B	$CH_3CH_2CH_3$	231	yes	0.0	300
C	CF_3CCl_2H	302	no	0.02	3000

(ODP is an abbreviation for ozone-depletion factor.)

*HCFAs are also known as HCFCs (hydrochlorofluorocarbons).
†HFAs are also known as HFCs (hydrofluorocarbons).

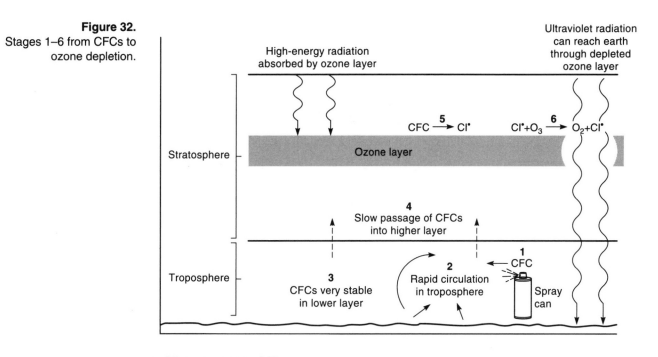

Figure 32.
Stages 1–6 from CFCs to ozone depletion.

a Name compound C.

b Suggest why compound B is very much cheaper than the others.

c Suggest why compound B can be used as a propellant and as a blowing agent but cannot be used as a cleaning solvent.

d The following reactions represent the first steps in the removal of HFAs and HCFAs from the atmosphere using compound C as an example.

$$H_2O \rightarrow H + OH \qquad \text{(equation 7.1)}$$

$$CF_3CCl_2H + OH \rightarrow CF_3CCl_2 + H_2O \qquad \text{(equation 7.2)}$$

   i) Draw a dot-and-cross diagram which explains why OH is a free radical.

   ii) Give the formula of another free radical in equation (7.1) or equation (7.2).

   iii) Explain why equation (7.2) is called a **propagation step**.

e The first step in the breakdown of CFCs in the atmosphere is thought to be splitting of a C—Cl bond by sunlight. For example, using compound A: $CFCl_3 \rightarrow CFCl_2\bullet + Cl\bullet$. This reaction initiates a series of processes in which free radicals cause the destruction of ozone in the stratosphere.

   Use information contained in this question, or other background knowledge, to explain why chemists expected HFAs and HCFAs to have lower ODPs than CFCs.

f You are a research worker who has just developed a method for producing compound C. Write a brief report to the head of your section explaining the usefulness of your compound together with any drawbacks.

As we have seen in the last exercise, the best alternatives to CFCs at the moment are hydrofluoroalkanes (HFAs). With no chlorine they have zero ODP. The drawback to these compounds is that they are expensive to make and have not been tested for safety or for their environmental effect.

In order to test whether you have understood and learnt this section on halogen compounds you should attempt the following Teacher-marked Exercise (**without** referring to your notes!).

EXERCISE

Teacher-marked

a Explain the following giving equations, mechanisms and details of products where possible.
  i) Halogenoalkanes react mostly by nucleophilic substitution.
  ii) Halogenoalkanes undergo elimination reactions with ethanolic alkali (the mechanism is **not** required).
  iii) Chloroalkanes are readily hydrolysed whereas chloroarenes are difficult to hydrolyse.

b Give a brief account of the uses, including reference to their advantages and disadvantages, of fluoroalkanes and fluorohalogenoalkanes. (Hint: Your answer should include CFCs and their partially halogenated alternatives.)

You have now completed the first organic volume. Much of the chemistry you have learned will be a foundation for what is to come later.

■ End-of-unit test

To find out how well you have learned the material in this volume, try the test which follows. Read the notes below before starting.
1. You should spend about 90 minutes on this test.
2. Hand your answers to your teacher for marking.

1. 2-Methylheptane and 2,2,4-trimethylpentane are isomers of octane. All three compounds are found in petrol. Which one of the following lists these isomers in order of increasing volatility?

A	Octane	2-Methylheptane	2,2,4-Trimethylpentane
B	Octane	2,2,4-Trimethylpentane	2-Methylheptane
C	2-Methylheptane	Octane	2,2,4-Trimethylpentane
D	2,2,4-Trimethylpentane	2-Methylheptane	Octane
E	2,2,4-Trimethylpentane	Octane	2-Methylheptane (1)

Questions 2–5 concern the following organic reaction mechanisms:
A electrophilic addition,
B electrophilic substitution,
C free radical substitution,
D nucleophilic addition,
E nucleophilic substitution.

Select from A to E, the mechanism by which the following substances would react under the conditions stated.

2. Methane and chlorine are mixed in bright sunlight. (1)
3. Ethene is passed into liquid bromine in the dark. (1)
4. Benzene is warmed with a mixture of concentrated nitric acid and concentrated sulphuric acid. (1)
5. 1-Bromobutane reacts with hot aqueous potassium hydroxide. (1)

A

6. The structural formula for 2-chloro-5,5-dimethylhexane is

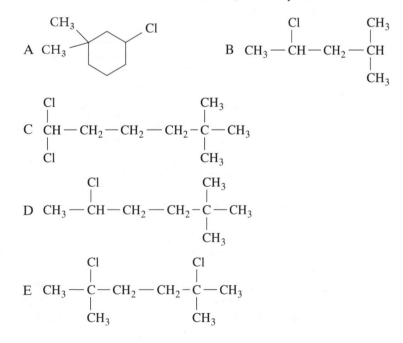

(1)

Questions 7–9

The following terms may be used to describe the shape of the **carbon skeleton** in organic molecules:

A rectangular planar,
B polygonal planar,
C linear,
D pyramidal,
E 'chair-shaped'.

Select the most appropriate term for

7. 2-methylpropane, (1)
8. 2,3-dimethylbut-2-ene, $(CH_3)_2C{=}C(CH_3)_2$, (1)
9. cyclohexane. (1)

Questions 10–12 concern the following hydrocarbons:

A ethene,
B methane,
C benzene,
D cyclohexane,
E cyclohexene.

Select, from A to E, the hydrocarbon which
10. is a liquid at 20°C and does not combine with hydrogen even in the presence of nickel, (1)
11. is formed when ethanol vapour is passed over aluminium oxide at 200°C, (1)
12. is a liquid at 20°C and reacts in two different ways with chlorine, depending on the conditions. (1)

Questions 13–17 (five questions)

For each of the questions below, **one** or **more** of the responses is (are) correct. Decide which of the responses is (are) correct. Then choose

A if **1**, **2** and **3** are correct,
B if **1** and **2** only are correct,
C if **2** and **3** only are correct,
D if **1** only is correct,
E if **3** only is correct.

Directions summarised				
A	B	C	D	E
1, 2, 3	**1, 2**	**2, 3**	**1**	**3**
correct	only	only	only	only

13. Correct statements about the $C{=}C$ bond in ethene include:
    1 the bond energy is twice that of $C{-}C$,
    2 it consists of two π-bonds,
    3 it has four shared electrons. (1)
14. Under one set of conditions, chlorine is found to attack the methyl group in methylbenzene, whereas under another set of conditions chlorine attaches itself to the benzene nucleus.
    Correct statements about the above data include:
    1 chlorination of the side-chain occurs by a free-radical mechanism,
    2 chlorine acts as an electrophile when it attacks the benzene ring,
    3 methylbenzene undergoes addition reactions with chlorine. (1)

15. In the free radical chlorination of methane the following two propagation steps alternate in a chain reaction:

$$Cl\bullet + CH_4 \rightarrow HCl + CH_3\bullet \qquad\qquad CH_3\bullet + Cl_2 \rightarrow CH_3Cl + Cl\bullet$$

Which of the following would be formed in a step which terminates this chain?
1 CH_2CH_2,
2 CH_3CH_3,
3 CH_3Cl. (1)

16. Industrial ethanol in the U.K. is now produced by the direct hydration of ethene, and this process has largely replaced the older fermentation route. Which of the following is/are likely to be reasons for this change?
1 The direct hydration route produces virtually pure ethanol rather than a dilute aqueous solution.
2 The direct hydration route produces ethanol by a faster reaction.
3 The direct hydration route employs milder conditions. (1)

17. Chlorofluorocarbons (CFCs) used in aerosols and refrigerators have been linked with the decrease in the concentration of trioxygen (ozone) in the stratosphere. Assuming that the CFC molecules are broken down by ultraviolet light into chlorine atoms, which then react as follows:

$$Cl + O_3 \rightarrow ClO + O_2$$

$$ClO + O \rightarrow Cl + O_2$$

which of the following statements concerning these two steps is/are correct?
1 Both Cl and O atoms have an odd number of electrons.
2 The Cl atoms act as a catalyst.
3 $O + O_3 \rightarrow 2O_2$ is the overall reaction. (1)

18. Write the full structural formulae of the following compounds:
a 3-ethyl-4-methylheptane,
b *cis*-pent-2-ene,
c propa-1,2-diene,
d 2-bromo-2-methylpropane. (4)

19. a A number of compounds resulting from man's chemical activities are known to cause atmospheric pollution. In the table below, give the names and formulae of any four atmospheric pollutants, stating the effect of the pollution from each.

Name and formula of pollutant	Effect of pollutant
i)	
ii)	
iii)	
iv)	

b For one of the pollutants in your table suggest a method of reducing its release into the atmosphere. (10)

20. Compare and contrast the chemistry of benzene and alkenes by commenting on the following observations:
    i)   The carbon–carbon bond length in benzene is 139 pm and that of ethene is 133 pm. (5)
    ii) Both benzene and ethene react with bromine, but the conditions and type of reaction are different. (5)
    iii) Benzene can be used as the solvent in some reactions involving $KMnO_4$ but the liquid alkene cyclohexene cannot. (3)

21. In the scheme below, name the reagents represented by the letters **A** to **G** inclusive and state the conditions under which each of the reactions takes place.

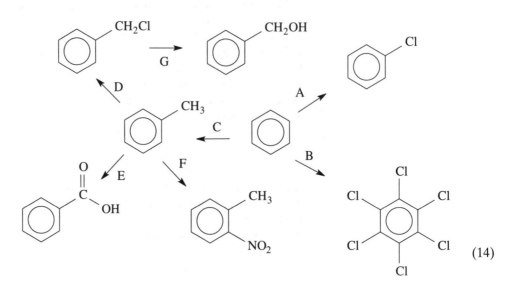

(14)

22. Compound A undergoes the following reactions:

$$A \xrightarrow[\text{trichloroethane}]{\text{bromine in}} CH_3CHBrCHBrCH_3 \xrightarrow{\text{II}} CH_2{=}CH{-}CH{=}CH_2$$

    I

a Suggest a structural formula for A.
b What type of reaction is step II? Suggest the conditions and reagents necessary to carry it out. (4)

23. Table 24 below shows a possible blend for unleaded petrol.

Table 24

Component	%	Contribution to cost	Octane rating	Contribution to octane rating	E70	Contribution to E70
Butane	7	0.3	71	5	100	7
Crackate	20	1.4	98	20	50	10
Straight run	15	0.75	71	11	95	15
Reformate	48	3.8	95	46	10	5
MTBE	10	1.0	118	12	0	0
Total	100	7.25		94		37

Straight run gasoline is the normal unprocessed gasoline fraction obtained from the distillation of crude oil. Reformate and crackate are the products of catalytic reforming and cracking respectively. MTBE is the ether 2-methoxy-2-methylpentane. E70 measures volatility.

In which of the categories **crackate, reformate, straight run** would you expect to find

  a i) cyclohexane,

     ii) heptane,

     iii) pent-1-ene? (3)

  b Explain why reformate has a higher octane number than straight run gasoline. (2)

  c E70 measures volatility and for this particular blend must be in the range 20–40. (High E70 values correspond to high volatility.) Suggest **one** method a chemist could use to make a small improvement in the octane rating of petrol without making E70 too large. Give a brief explanation for your answer. (3)

(Total: 70 marks)

ANSWERS

(Answers to questions from examination papers are provided by ILPAC and not by the examination boards.)

EXERCISE 1
a Nitro.
b Ether.
c Double bond and chloro.
d Hydroxy.
e Benzene ring and nitrile.
f Carbonyl and amino.

EXERCISE 2
a Benzene ring, carboxyl, ester.
b Benzene ring, hydroxy, amide (secondary, i.e. —CONH— rather than —CONH$_2$)
c Benzene ring (2), chloro (3).
d Benzene ring and nitro (3).
e Amide (tertiary, i.e. —CON< rather than —CONH$_2$), double bond (2), amino (one secondary, one tertiary), benzene ring.
f Benzene ring, ester, amino (tertiary).
g Benzene ring (3), ester, hydroxy (2).
h Benzene ring, chloro (3), ether, carboxyl.
i Benzene ring (2), chloro (4), ether (2).
j Benzene ring (2), chloro, amide (tertiary – see e). There is also another functional group, >C=N—, which is not included in our list.
k Amino, carboxyl. There is also a group consisting of the anion of a carboxyl group, —CO$_2^-$.

EXERCISE 3
a The higher member has an extra —CH$_2$ group in its carbon chain.
b 1 and 3; 2 and 4; 5 and 9; 6 and 10; 7 and 8.

EXERCISE 4
a A cycloalkane.
b An alkane.
c An alkene.
d An alkylbenzene.

EXERCISE 5 a

Table 4

	Molecular formula	Structural formula
Methane	CH_4	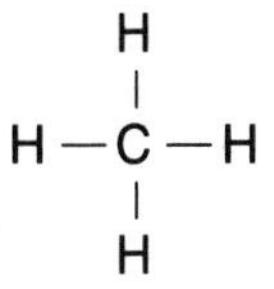 H | H — C — H | H
Ethane	C_2H_6	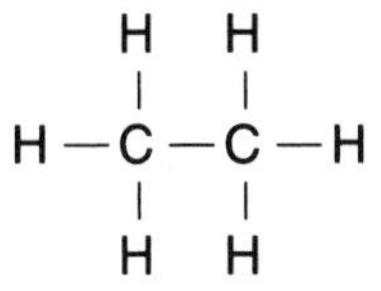 H H | | H — C — C — H | | H H
Propane	C_3H_8	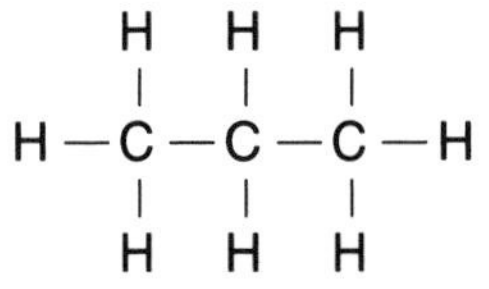 H H H | | | H — C — C — C — H | | | H H H
Butane	C_4H_{10}	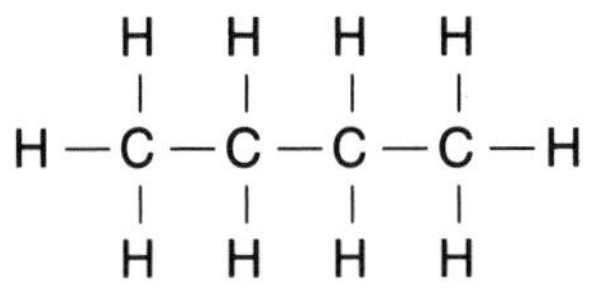 H H H H | | | | H — C — C — C — C — H | | | | H H H H
Pentane	C_5H_{12}	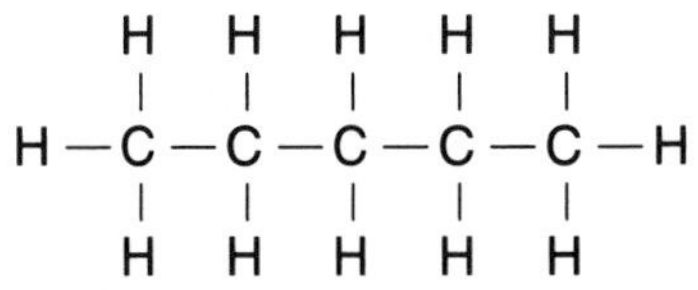 H H H H H | | | | | H — C — C — C — C — C — H | | | | | H H H H H
Hexane	C_6H_{14}	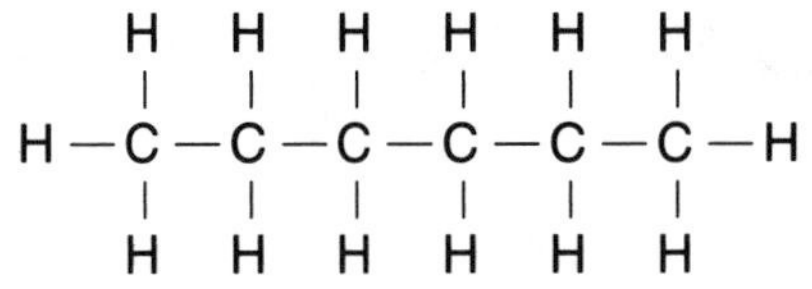 H H H H H H | | | | | | H — C — C — C — C — C — C — H | | | | | | H H H H H H
Heptane	C_7H_{16}	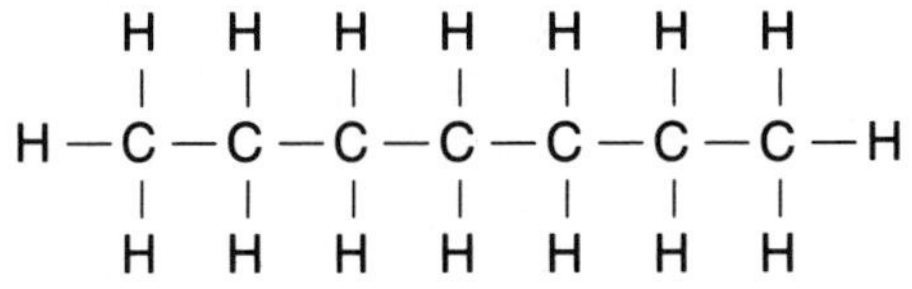 H H H H H H H | | | | | | | H — C — C — C — C — C — C — C — H | | | | | | | H H H H H H H

b C_nH_{2n+2}

c $C_{12}H_{26}$

EXERCISE 6 **a** Tetrahedral.

b

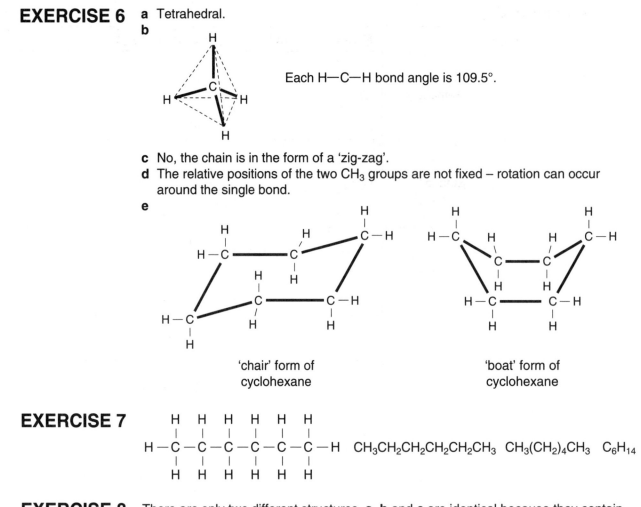

Each H—C—H bond angle is 109.5°.

c No, the chain is in the form of a 'zig-zag'.

d The relative positions of the two CH_3 groups are not fixed – rotation can occur around the single bond.

e

'chair' form of cyclohexane

'boat' form of cyclohexane

EXERCISE 7

$$H-\underset{\underset{H}{|}}{\overset{\overset{H}{|}}{C}}-\underset{\underset{H}{|}}{\overset{\overset{H}{|}}{C}}-\underset{\underset{H}{|}}{\overset{\overset{H}{|}}{C}}-\underset{\underset{H}{|}}{\overset{\overset{H}{|}}{C}}-\underset{\underset{H}{|}}{\overset{\overset{H}{|}}{C}}-\underset{\underset{H}{|}}{\overset{\overset{H}{|}}{C}}-H$$

$CH_3CH_2CH_2CH_2CH_2CH_3$ $CH_3(CH_2)_4CH_3$ C_6H_{14}

EXERCISE 8 There are only two different structures. **a**, **b** and **c** are identical because they contain the same unbranched 4-carbon-atom chain. **d** has a branched chain.

EXERCISE 9   a

Table 5

Molecular formula	Structural formula of straight chain	Were any other arrangements possible? If yes, draw their structural formulae
CH_4	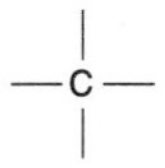	No
C_2H_6	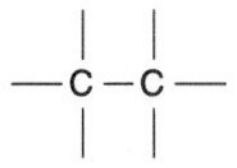	No
C_3H_8	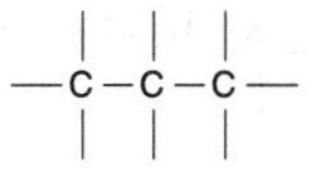	No
C_4H_{10}	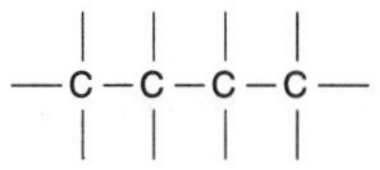	Yes 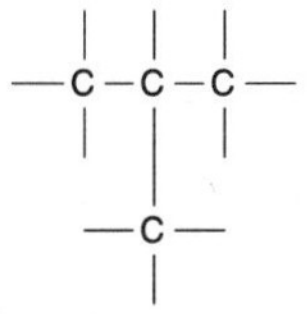
C_5H_{12}	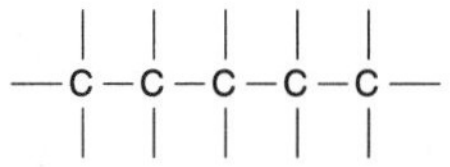	Yes 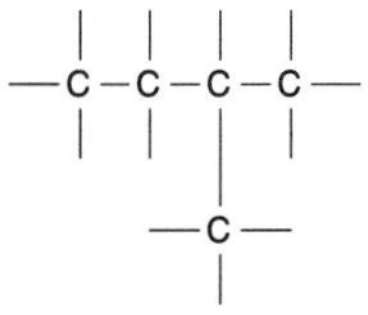 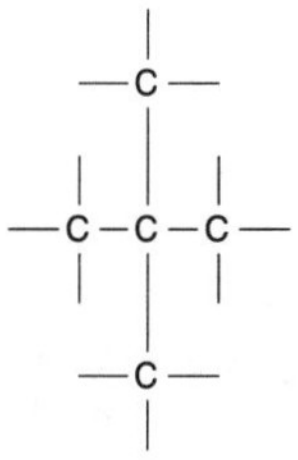
C_6H_{14}	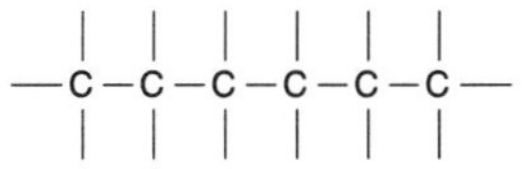	Yes 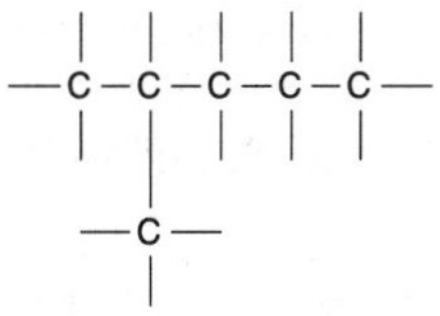 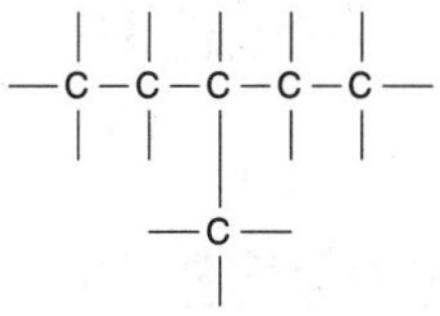 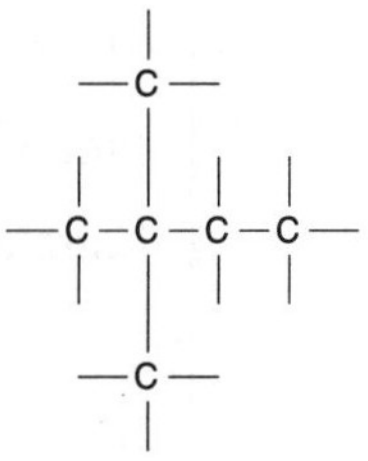 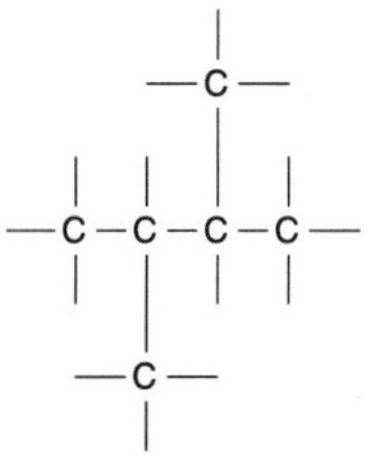

b CH_4, C_2H_6 and C_3H_8 have no isomers.

EXERCISE 10

a 2,2-Dimethylbutane

b 3-Ethyl-2,4-dimethylpentane

c 2,3,4-Trimethylhexane

d 3-Ethyl-2-methylheptane

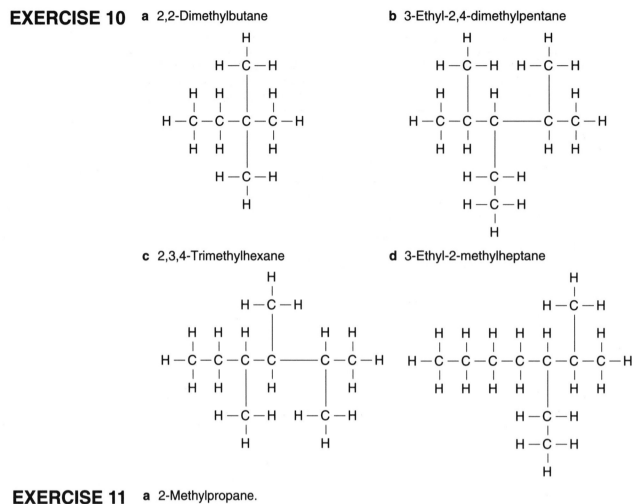

EXERCISE 11
a 2-Methylpropane.
b 4-Ethylheptane.
c 3-Methylheptane.

EXERCISE 12
a 2,2-Dimethylpropane.
b 2,3-Dimethylhexane.
c 4-Ethyl-3,5-dimethyloctane.

EXERCISE 13

Table 6

Formula	Name	Boiling point/K	Melting point/K	Density/g cm^{-3}	
CH_4	methane	112	90.7	0.424	Density of liquid at boiling point
C_2H_6	ethane	185	89.9	0.546	
C_3H_8	propane	231	85.5	0.582	
C_4H_{10}	butane	273	135	0.579	
C_5H_{12}	pentane	309	143	0.626	
C_6H_{14}	hexane	342	178	0.659	
C_7H_{16}	heptane	372	183	0.684	
C_8H_{18}	octane	399	216	0.703	
C_9H_{20}	nonane	424	220	0.718	
$C_{10}H_{22}$	decane	447	243	0.730	

a The values of each physical property show a general increase with increased molar mass.

b

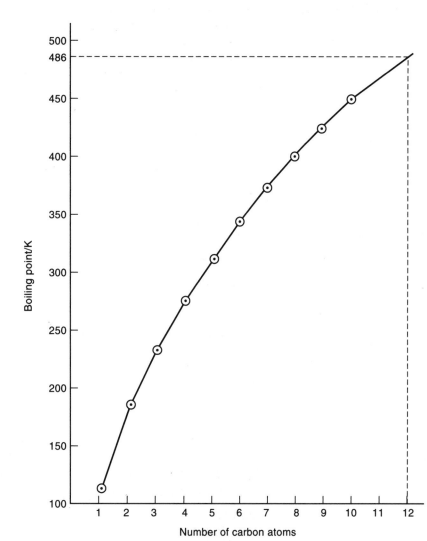

The boiling points of alkanes increase with chain length. This is a result not of increasing mass but of increasing polarisability. A molecule with high relative molecular mass contains a large number of electrons and therefore forms temporary dipoles more readily than a molecule with a smaller number of electrons.

As chain length increases, an increase of one carbon atom becomes less and less significant as a proportion of the whole; the increase in boiling point therefore becomes smaller.

c 486 K (see graph).

d i) The increases in melting point are less regular than the increases in boiling point, but from butane to decane average about 18 K, decreasing. This suggests that a melting point greater than 293 K (20°C) would be reached by adding about four more C atoms, i.e. at $C_{14}H_{30}$.

   ii) The increases in density from pentane onwards are, in g cm^{-3}, 0.033, 0.025, 0.019, 0.015 and 0.012. Four further increases might be 0.010, 0.009, 0.008 and 0.007, giving the density of $C_{14}H_{30}$ as 0.764 g dm^{-3}.

EXERCISE 14 All the statements except **b** are general characteristics of a homologous series.

EXERCISE 15 As branching in the molecule increases, the boiling point decreases. Pentane is a linear molecule whereas 2,2-dimethylpropane approximates to a sphere. The effective surface area available for interaction between two pentane molecules is greater than that available between two molecules of 2,2-dimethylpropane. Thus, the van der Waals forces between pentane molecules are greater than those between 2,2-dimethylpropane molecules, accounting for the higher boiling point. 2-Methylbutane represents the intermediate situation.

EXERCISE 16 **a** $\bar{E}$ (C—C) (general) = 346 kJ mol^{-1}
$\bar{E}$ (C—H) (general) = 413 kJ mol^{-1}
These values are higher than most of the other single bonds listed.
b The high C—C and C—H bond energies suggest that the alkanes are potentially unreactive compounds.

EXPERIMENT 1

Specimen results
Results Table 1

Reaction	Observations
A. **Combustion**	
Appearance of flame	Orange and blue flame.
Sootiness	Very little soot.
B. **Action of bromine** (in inert solvent)	
1. In dark.	1. Liquids mix. No other change.
2. In light.	1. Liquids mix and decolorise. Steamy gas evolved.
Identification of gas	Damp blue litmus paper turns red. White fumes with ammonia stopper. (HBr produced.)
C. **Action of acidified potassium manganate(VII)**	No reaction. Liquids remain separate.
D. **Action of concentrated sulphuric acid**	No reaction. Liquids remain separate.

Questions
1. Yes, cyclohexane fails to react with three powerful reagents, and reacts with a fourth only in the presence of light.
2. **a** Carbon dioxide and water.
   b CH_4 (g) + $2O_2$ (g) → CO_2 (g) + $2H_2O$ (l); $\Delta H^\ominus$ = −890 kJ mol^{-1}
      $2C_2H_6$ (g) + $7O_2$ (g) → $4CO_2$ (g) + $6H_2O$ (l); $\Delta H^\ominus$ = −3120 kJ mol^{-1}
   or C_2H_6 (g) + $3\frac{1}{2}O_2$ (g) → $2CO_2$ (g) + $3H_2O$ (l); $\Delta H^\ominus$ = −1560 kJ mol^{-1}
      C_3H_8 (g) + $5O_2$ (g) → $3CO_2$ (g) + $4H_2O$ (l); $\Delta H^\ominus$ = −2220 kJ mol^{-1}
   c The highly exothermic combustion reactions of alkanes make them valuable as fuels.
3. **a** In a substitution reaction, one atom (or group of atoms) in a molecule is replaced by another atom (or group).
   b

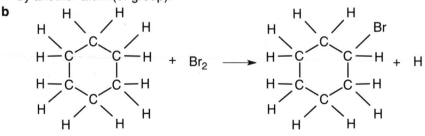

c Ultraviolet light. ('Light' alone is **not** good enough. It must be ultraviolet light.)

d $CH_4 + Br_2 \rightarrow CH_3Br + HBr$ bromomethane
$CH_3Br + Br_2 \rightarrow CH_2Br_2 + HBr$ dibromomethane
$CH_2Br_2 + Br_2 \rightarrow CHBr_3 + HBr$ tribromomethane
$CHBr_3 + Br_2 \rightarrow CBr_4 + HBr$ tetrabromomethane

EXERCISE 17

a   i) Homolytic,
    ii) Free radical.
b   i) Heterolytic,
    ii) Positive; carbocation,
    iii) Negative; carbanion.
c   Nucleophiles; electrophiles.

EXERCISE 18

a

(1) Homolytic fission   (2) and (3) Heterolytic fission

b (3) is the most likely because in HCl, chlorine is more electronegative than hydrogen and already has a strong attraction for the bonding electrons.

EXERCISE 19

a and d are free radicals. b and c are carbocations.
e is a carbanion.

EXERCISE 20

Nucleophiles	Electrophiles
Br^-	I^+
ROH*	NO_2^+
RO^-	H^+
H^-	Cl^+
RCO_2^-	
NH_3*	
OH^-	
H_2O*	
Cl^-	
CN^-	
I^-	

*These uncharged molecules are nucleophilic because their lone pair(s) of electrons are attracted towards a positive charge.

EXERCISE 21

The methyl radicals produced by thermal decomposition of tetramethyl lead(IV) react with chlorine molecules to produce chlorine radicals

$$CH_3\bullet + Cl_2 \rightarrow CH_3Cl + Cl\bullet$$

in the absence of light, followed by the reaction:

$$Cl\bullet + CH_4 \rightarrow HCl + CH_3\bullet$$

and so on.
This supports the proposed mechanism.

EXERCISE 22   **Table 8** Mechanism for chlorination of methane

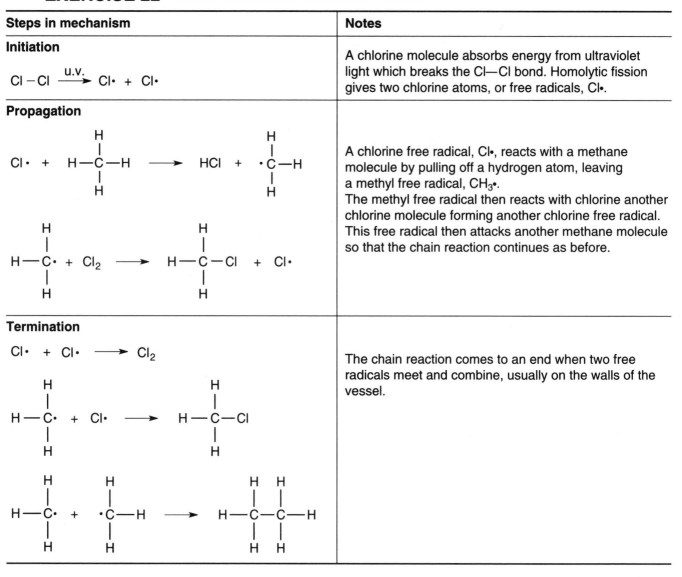

Steps in mechanism	Notes
Initiation	A chlorine molecule absorbs energy from ultraviolet light which breaks the Cl—Cl bond. Homolytic fission gives two chlorine atoms, or free radicals, Cl•.
Propagation	A chlorine free radical, Cl•, reacts with a methane molecule by pulling off a hydrogen atom, leaving a methyl free radical, CH_3•. The methyl free radical then reacts with chlorine another chlorine molecule forming another chlorine free radical. This free radical then attacks another methane molecule so that the chain reaction continues as before.
Termination	The chain reaction comes to an end when two free radicals meet and combine, usually on the walls of the vessel.

b Chlorine radicals, Cl•, can attack CH_3Cl molecules as well as CH_4, in the propagation steps:

$$Cl• + CH_4 \rightarrow CH_3• + HCl$$

$$Cl• + CH_3Cl \rightarrow CH_2Cl• + HCl$$

This provides another possible termination step:

$$CH_2Cl• + Cl• \rightarrow CH_2Cl_2$$

Similarly, further reactions can occur:

$$Cl• + CH_2Cl_2 \rightarrow CHCl_2• + HCl$$

$$Cl• + CHCl_2• \rightarrow CHCl_3$$

$$Cl• + CHCl_3 \rightarrow CCl_3• + HCl$$

$$Cl• + CCl_3• \rightarrow CCl_4$$

The greater the excess of chlorine, the smaller the concentration of CH_4 relative to CH_3Cl, CH_2Cl_2 and $CHCl_3$; therefore, further chlorination becomes more likely.

c The reaction can begin only when chlorine free radicals are formed by the dissociation of chlorine molecules, which requires a considerable input of energy. In the dark, no source of energy is available (except at high temperatures).

EXERCISE 23 a

Table 9	Name	Molecular formula	Structural formula
	Ethene	C_2H_4	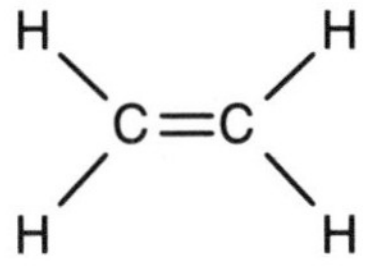 (see structure below)
	Propene	C_3H_6	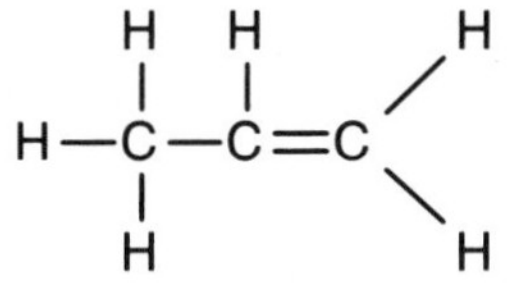 (see structure below)
	But-1-ene	C_4H_8	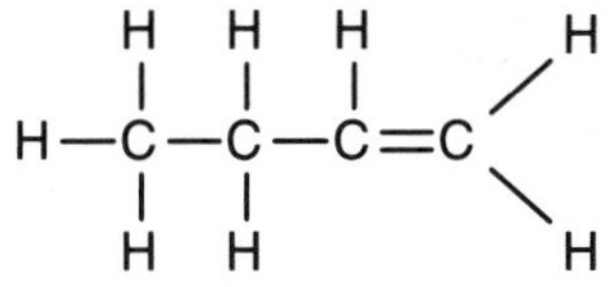 (see structure below)
	Pent-1-ene	C_5H_{10}	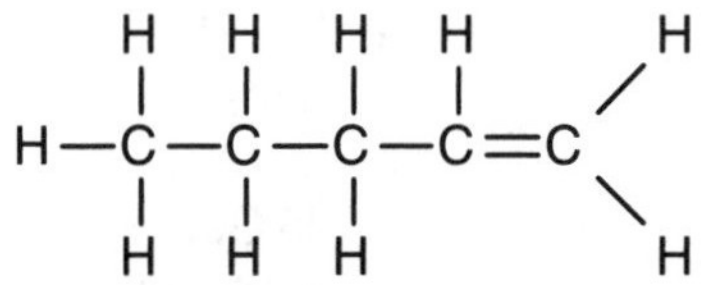 (see structure below)
	Hex-1-ene	C_6H_{12}	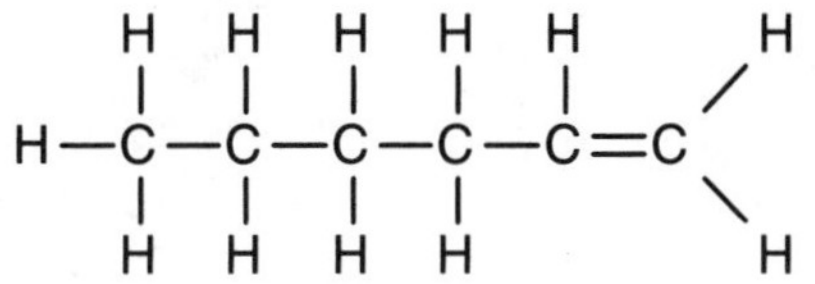 (see structure below)

b C_nH_{2n}

c The number in the name refers to the chain position of the doubly bonded carbon atom nearest the end of the chain. This number can only be '1' in propene, and it is therefore not necessary to include it.

EXERCISE 24 a

i) Hex-1-ene.
ii) Buta-1,2-diene.
iii) But-2-ene.
iv) 2-Methylbut-2-ene.

b i) 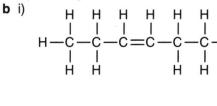 ii)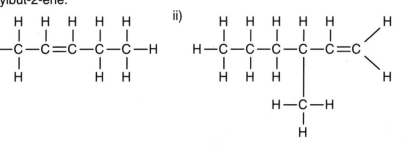

[continued overleaf]

iii)

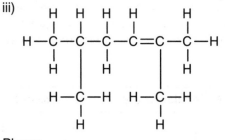

EXERCISE 25

a Planar.

b

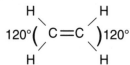

c The model of the molecule of ethene suggests that there cannot be rotation about the C=C bond.

EXERCISE 26 No, because free rotation is not possible about the double bond.

EXERCISE 27

a

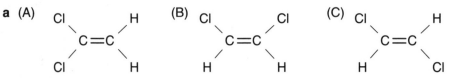

b i) and ii) Structural isomerism. (This type of structural isomerism is sometimes called 'positional isomerism' because the same functional groups appear in different positions on the carbon chain.)
iii) Geometrical isomerism (*cis–trans* isomerism).

c (A) 1,1-dichloroethene,
(B) *cis*-1,2-dichloroethene,
(C) *trans*-1,2-dichloroethene.

d In structural isomerism, the isomers have the same molecular formula but differ in structure, i.e. in the order in which the different atoms are linked. In geometrical isomerism the isomers have the same molecular formula and also show the same order in which the different atoms are linked. However, their arrangement in space is different.

EXERCISE 28

a i) *trans*-pent-2-ene,
ii) *cis*-1,2-dibromoethene,
iii) *trans*-hex-3-ene.

b

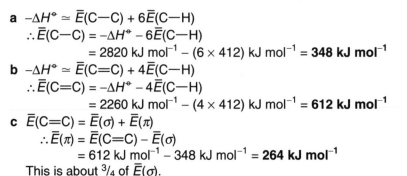

EXERCISE 29

a $-\Delta H^{\ominus} \simeq \bar{E}(\text{C—C}) + 6\bar{E}(\text{C—H})$
$\therefore \bar{E}(\text{C—C}) = -\Delta H^{\ominus} - 6\bar{E}(\text{C—H})$
$= 2820 \text{ kJ mol}^{-1} - (6 \times 412) \text{ kJ mol}^{-1} = \textbf{348 kJ mol}^{-1}$

b $-\Delta H^{\ominus} \simeq \bar{E}(\text{C}=\text{C}) + 4\bar{E}(\text{C—H})$
$\therefore \bar{E}(\text{C}=\text{C}) = -\Delta H^{\ominus} - 4\bar{E}(\text{C—H})$
$= 2260 \text{ kJ mol}^{-1} - (4 \times 412) \text{ kJ mol}^{-1} = \textbf{612 kJ mol}^{-1}$

c $\bar{E}(\text{C}=\text{C}) = \bar{E}(\sigma) + \bar{E}(\pi)$
$\therefore \bar{E}(\pi) = \bar{E}(\text{C}=\text{C}) - \bar{E}(\sigma)$
$= 612 \text{ kJ mol}^{-1} - 348 \text{ kJ mol}^{-1} = \textbf{264 kJ mol}^{-1}$
This is about $^3/_4$ of $\bar{E}(\sigma)$.

d It requires less energy to break the π-bond in ethene than the σ-bond in ethane. This suggests that ethene might be more reactive than ethane.

EXPERIMENT 2
Specimen results
Results Table 2

Reaction	Observations
A. **Combustion**	
Appearance of flame	Orange and blue flame.
Sootiness	Slightly sooty.
B. **Action of bromine** (in inert solvent)	
1. In dark.	1. Liquids mix and decolorise.
2. In light.	2. Liquids mix and decolorise.
Identification of gas	No gas is given off.
C. **Action of acidified potassium manganate(VII)**	Rapid decolorisation. Liquids remain separate.
D. **Action of concentrated sulphuric acid**	Liquids mix and react vigorously. Colour darkens to charred black mass.

1. Yes. A comparison of the results for Experiments 1 and 2 shows more positive reactions for cyclohexene than cyclohexane, indicating the greater reactivity of alkenes in general.
2. The presence of soot in the flame is an indication of the higher carbon to hydrogen ratio in alkenes than in alkanes. Each C atom requires two O atoms for complete combustion whereas two H atoms require only one O atom.
3. Unlike alkanes, alkenes decolorise bromine in the absence of light and acidified potassium manganate(VII) solution.

EXERCISE 30
a $CH_2{=}CH_2 + Br_2 \rightarrow CH_2BrCH_2Br$ (room temperature – usually in
                            1,2-dibromoethane   an inert solvent)
b $CH_2{=}CH_2 + H_2O + [O] \rightarrow CH_2OHCH_2OH$ (room temperature, $KMnO_4$)
                                 ethane-1,2-diol
                                (ethylene glycol)
c $CH_2{=}CH_2 + H_2SO_4 \rightarrow C_2H_5OSO_2OH$ (room temperature)
                            ethyl hydrogensulphate
$C_2H_5OSO_2OH + H_2O \rightarrow C_2H_5OH + H_2SO_4$ (heat)
                               ethanol

EXERCISE 31
a $CH_2{=}CH_2 + HBr \rightarrow CH_3CH_2Br$ (room temperature, gas phase
                            bromoethane   or concentrated acid)
b $CH_3CH{=}CHCH_3 + H_2 \rightarrow C_4H_{10}$ (150°C, nickel catalyst)
                              butane

EXERCISE 32
a Polyethene (polythene).
b $nCH_2{=}CH_2 \rightarrow ({-}CH_2{-}CH_2{-})_n$ polyethene.
c Polymerisation.
d i) 1500 atm, 200°C, trace of oxygen as catalyst.
    ii) 3 atm, 50°C, Ziegler catalyst (triethyl aluminium, $(C_2H_5)_3Al$, and titanium chloride).

EXERCISE 33

Table 10
Ethene-based polymers

Group Y in monomer CH$_2$=CHY	Structural formula of trimer (n = 3)	Repeating unit	Name(s) of polymer	Uses
—H	H—C—C—C—C—C—C—H (with H above and below each C)	—C—C— (with H above and below)	poly(ethene) (polyethylene) (polythene)	plastic bags, squeezy bottles, buckets, washing-up bowls
—CH$_3$	H—C—C—C—C—C—C—H (H, CH$_3$H, CH$_3$H, CH$_3$)	—C—C— (H, CH$_3$)	poly(propene) (polypropylene)	crates, clothing, carpets, ropes and twine, pipes
—Cl	H—C—C—C—C—C—C—H (H, Cl, H, Cl, H, Cl)	—C—C— (H, Cl)	poly(chloroethene) (polyvinylchloride) (PVC)	raincoats, guttering, records, floor-tiles
—CN	H—C—C—C—C—C—C—H (H, CN, H, CN, H, CN)	—C—C— (H, CN)	poly(propenenitrile) (polyacrylonitrile) (Acrilan)	making textiles (wool substitute)
phenyl group	H—C—C—C—C—C—C—H (with phenyl groups)	—C—C— (H, phenyl)	poly(phenylethene) (polystyrene)	rigid (but brittle!) boxes, pots, toys, etc. Insulation and packaging (as a foam)
—O—C(=O)—CH$_3$	H—C—C—C—C—C—C—H (with O—C(=O)CH$_3$ groups)	—C—C— (H, O—C(=O)CH$_3$)	poly(ethenyl-ethanoate) (polyvinylacetate) (PVA)	glue

EXERCISE 34   Structure **a**.

EXERCISE 35   **a**

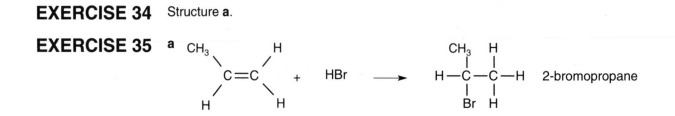

2-bromopropane

b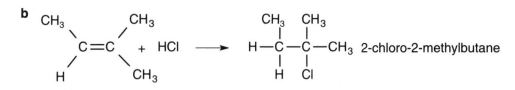

EXERCISE 36

Table 11
Mechanism for the
bromination of ethene **a**

Step 1. Initiation Br — Br $\longrightarrow$ $\overset{\delta^+}{Br} — \overset{\delta^-}{Br}$	The bromine molecule becomes polarised as it approaches the region of high electron density in the double bond.
Step 2. Formation of intermediate* H—C=C—H $\longrightarrow$ H—C—C—H + Br⁻	The Br$^{\delta+}$ (electrophile) and the electrons on the double bond are attracted to one another. One bonding pair in the double bond shifts to form a C—Br bond, leaving the other C atom with a positive charge. The bonding pair in the Br—Br bond becomes a lone pair on a bromide ion.
Step 3. Termination H—C—C—H $\longrightarrow$ H—C—C—H	The positive carbocation and the negative bromide ion are attracted to one another and form the final product by making a covalent bond.

b Step 2 is the slow attack of the electrophile Br$^{\delta+}$ to the ethene molecule.
   Step 3 is the fast attack of the nucleophile Br⁻ to the intermediate carbocation.
      Since the rate of the overall reaction is governed by the slower or 'rate-determining step', the whole process is known as electrophilic addition.
      An alternative mechanism has been proposed which involves the formation of a bromonium ion as an intermediate.

EXERCISE 37 a **Step 1.   Initiation**

$$H_2SO_4 \rightarrow \overset{\delta^+}{H} — \overset{\delta^-}{O}SO_2OH$$

(Because of electronegativity differences, this polarisation is always present in the H_2SO_4 molecule, but it is increased on approaching the double bond.)

Step 2.   Formation of reactive intermediate

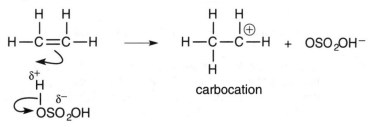

Step 3. Termination

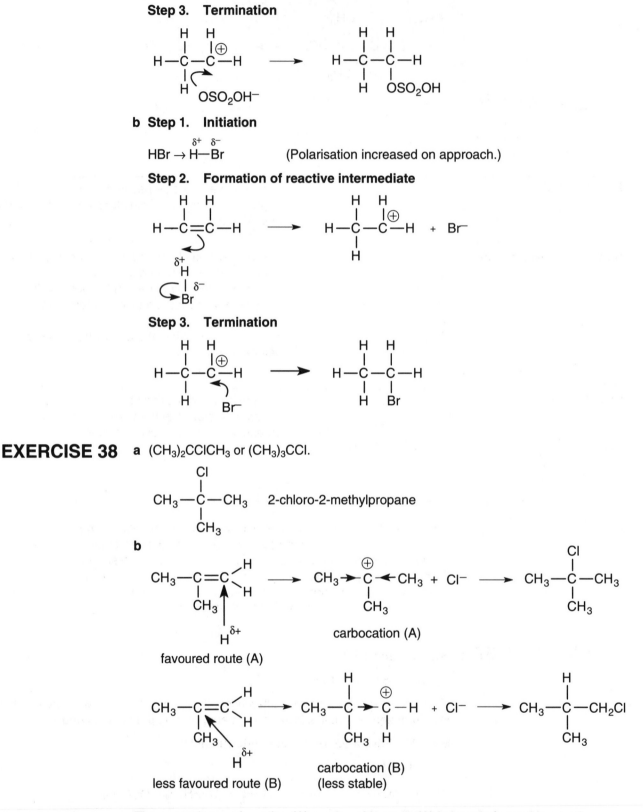

b Step 1. Initiation

$$HBr \rightarrow \overset{\delta^+ \ \delta^-}{H-Br}$$ (Polarisation increased on approach.)

Step 2. Formation of reactive intermediate

Step 3. Termination

EXERCISE 38   **a** $(CH_3)_2CClCH_3$ or $(CH_3)_3CCl$.

$CH_3-\underset{\underset{CH_3}{|}}{\overset{\overset{Cl}{|}}{C}}-CH_3$ 2-chloro-2-methylpropane

b

favoured route (A)

carbocation (A)

less favoured route (B)

carbocation (B)
(less stable)

The secondary carbocation (A) produced in route (A) is largely formed in practice because of its greater stability. Two electron-releasing alkyl groups are more effective than one in stabilising the ion by delocalising the charge. The chloride ion then attacks this ion to produce 2-chloro-2-methylpropane.

EXERCISE 39   Markownikoff's rule states that the hydrogen atom in the electrophile will add to the carbon atom which already has the more hydrogen. In doing so, an extra alkyl group is created, which helps to stabilise the carbocation by delocalising the charge.

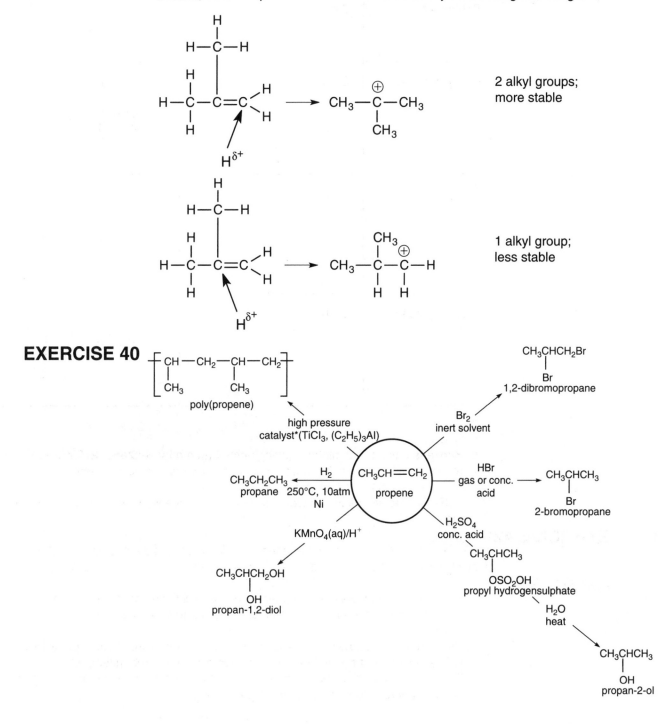

2 alkyl groups; more stable

1 alkyl group; less stable

EXERCISE 40

poly(propene)

high pressure
catalyst*(TiCl₃, (C₂H₅)₃Al)

CH_3CHCH_2Br
|
Br
1,2-dibromopropane

Br₂
inert solvent

propene

$CH_3CH=CH_2$

H₂
$CH_3CH_2CH_3$
propane   250°C, 10atm
Ni

HBr
gas or conc.
acid

CH_3CHCH_3
|
Br
2-bromopropane

KMnO₄(aq)/H⁺

H₂SO₄
conc. acid

CH_3CHCH_3
|
OSO_2OH
propyl hydrogensulphate

CH_3CHCH_2OH
|
OH
propan-1,2-diol

H₂O
heat

CH_3CHCH_3
|
OH
propan-2-ol

*This Ziegler–Natta catalyst operates by an ionic mechanism, not the free radical mechanism for addition polymerisation described in the Revealing Exercise earlier in the section.

EXERCISE 41

Table 12
Homologous series of arenes

Name	Molecular formula	Structural formula
Benzene	C_6H_6	
Methylbenzene	C_7H_8	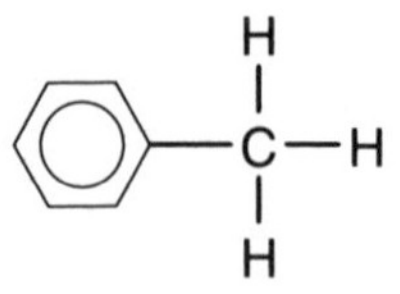
Ethylbenzene	C_8H_{10}	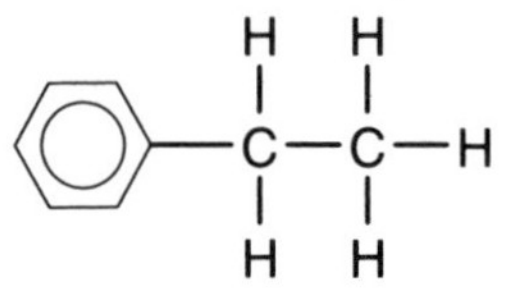
Propylbenzene	C_9H_{12}	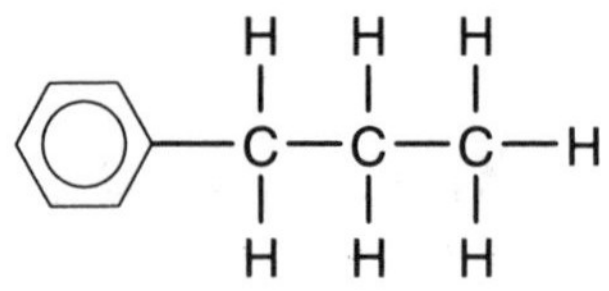

a

b C_nH_{2n-6}

c Benzene has a much higher melting point than methylbenzene (279 K and 178 K respectively) because the more compact symmetrical molecules of benzene pack more closely in a crystal lattice.

(Boiling points follow the usual pattern of increase with increasing number of electrons.)

EXERCISE 42

We expect the $C\cdots C$ bond in benzene to be less susceptible than the $C=C$ bond to electrophilic addition because the electron density is less.

EXERCISE 43

a Yes, benzene is resistant to reagents such as acidified potassium manganate(VII) and concentrated sulphuric acid which undergo addition with the $C=C$ bond in alkenes.

b Benzene produces a sootier flame than either cyclohexane, C_6H_{12}, or cyclohexene, C_6H_{10}, because of the higher carbon to hydrogen ratio in benzene, C_6H_6.

c The reaction with bromine in an inert solvent in the presence of iron appears to be a substitution reaction because HBr is produced.

$$R-H + Br_2 \rightarrow R-Br + HBr$$

The slight reaction with bromine in the light, with no evolution of HBr, suggests that this might be addition.

d i) Benzene reacts fairly readily with bromine in an inert solvent in the presence of iron filings; cyclohexane does not.

ii) Benzene does not react with bromine in an inert solvent; cyclohexene does.

EXERCISE 44

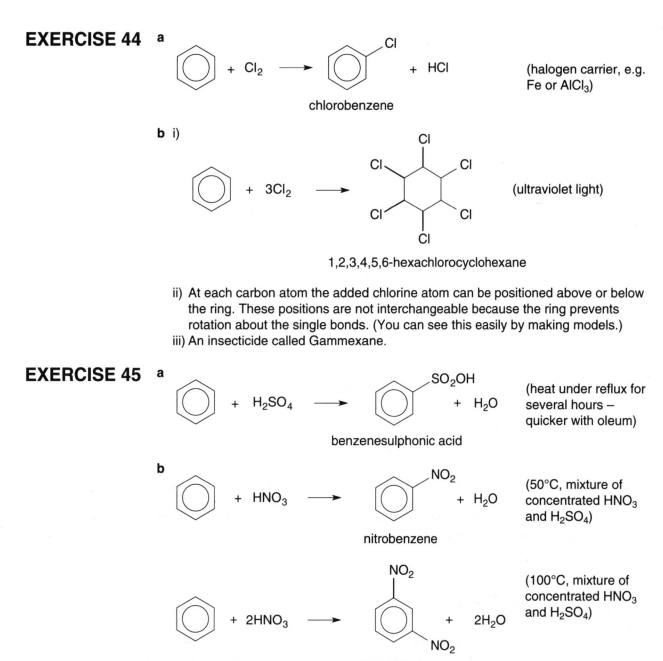

1,2,3,4,5,6-hexachlorocyclohexane

ii) At each carbon atom the added chlorine atom can be positioned above or below the ring. These positions are not interchangeable because the ring prevents rotation about the single bonds. (You can see this easily by making models.)

iii) An insecticide called Gammexane.

EXERCISE 45

benzenesulphonic acid

nitrobenzene

1,3-dinitrobenzene

EXERCISE 46 The delocalised ring of electrons in benzene gives the molecule stability. Benzene cannot undergo addition reactions and still retain the stable delocalised ring system. Instead, the majority of reactions of benzene involve substitution in the ring which leaves the stable delocalised system intact.

EXERCISE 47 a The iodine atom, I.

b Chlorine is more electronegative than iodine.

c The iodine has a partial positive charge: $I^{\delta+}-Cl^{\delta-}$

d Electrophilic substitution. The positive I atom is attracted to the delocalised rings of electrons and forms an unstable intermediate. This is followed by the expulsion of a proton, which retains the stable delocalised ring system.

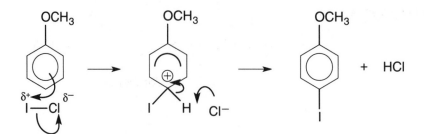

EXERCISE 48 **a** The active nitrating species is the nitryl cation (nitronium ion), NO_2^+.

$$HNO_3 + 2H_2SO_4 \rightarrow H_3O^+ + 2HSO_4^- + NO_2^+$$

b The nitryl cation, NO_2^+, is an electrophile which is attracted to the delocalised electron system in benzene to form an unstable intermediate. This is followed by the expulsion of a proton, which retains the stable delocalised ring system. This type of reaction is therefore called **electrophilic substitution**.

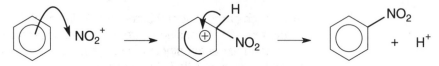

EXERCISE 49 **a** The attacking species in the bromination of benzene is the polarised bromine molecule, $Br^{\delta+}—Br^{\delta-}$.

Bromine molecules are polarised by halogen carriers such as $AlCl_3$ or $FeBr_3$ (produced when added iron reacts with bromine).

$$Br_2 + FeBr_3 \rightarrow Br^{\delta+}—Br^{\delta-}---FeBr_3$$

(Some texts give:

$$Br_2 + FeBr_3 \rightarrow Br^+ + FeBr_4^-)$$

b The positively charged bromine, $Br^{\delta+}$, acts as an electrophile which is attracted to the delocalised electron system in benzene to form an unstable intermediate. This is followed by the expulsion of a proton to form bromobenzene and regenerate the catalyst.

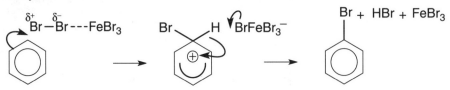

c The catalyst is either aluminium chloride, $AlCl_3$, or iron(III) bromide, $FeBr_3$. Its function is to withdraw electrons from the bond between the bromine atoms, i.e. to polarise the bromine molecule, in order that the positively charged bromine atom can then attack the benzene ring.

EXERCISE 50 **a** i)

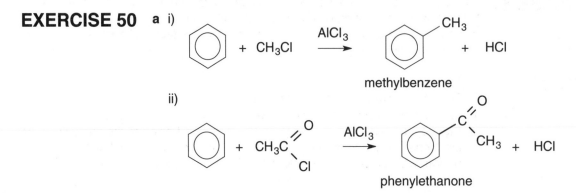

b Reaction **a** i) is called 'alkylation' (substitution of alkyl groups).

Reaction **a** ii) is called 'acylation' (substitution of acyl group).

c Reaction **a** i) proceeds by electrophilic substitution as follows:

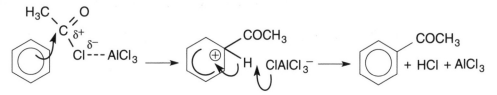

The catalyst, $AlCl_3$, withdraws the electrons from the C—Cl bond in chloromethane. The positively charged methyl group acts as an electrophile which is attracted to the benzene ring to form an unstable intermediate. This is followed by the expulsion of a proton to form methylbenzene and regenerate the catalyst.

The mechanism for reaction **a** ii), which also proceeds by electrophilic substitution, is similar to that described above.

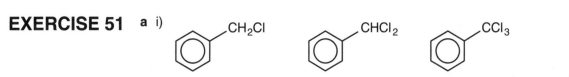

EXERCISE 51   **a** i)

These compounds are formed by progressive replacement of the hydrogen atoms of the side-chain by chlorine atoms.

ii) The function of the ultraviolet light is to split chlorine molecules into chlorine atoms (free radicals)

$$Cl_2 \xrightarrow[\text{u.v. light}]{} Cl\bullet + Cl\bullet$$

and this initiates the reaction.

iii) To protect the eyes from harmful ultraviolet light.

iv) Free radical substitution occurs, similar to that described for the chlorination of methane.

1. **Initiation**	$Cl_2 \rightarrow 2Cl\bullet$
2. **Propagation**	$C_6H_5CH_3 + Cl\bullet \rightarrow C_6H_5CH_2\bullet + HCl$
	$C_6H_5CH_2\bullet + Cl_2 \rightarrow C_6H_5CH_2Cl + Cl\bullet$
3. **Termination**	$Cl\bullet + Cl\bullet \rightarrow Cl_2$
	$C_6H_5CH_2\bullet + Cl\bullet \rightarrow C_6H_5CH_2Cl$
	$C_6H_5CH_2\bullet + C_6H_5CH_2\bullet \rightarrow C_6H_5CH_2CH_2C_6H_5$

If chlorine is passed through continuously, further propagation steps are possible as the concentration of $C_6H_5CH_2Cl$ increases.

$$C_6H_5CH_2Cl + Cl\bullet \rightarrow C_6H_5CHCl\bullet + HCl$$
$$C_6H_5CHCl\bullet + Cl_2 \rightarrow C_6H_5CHCl_2 + Cl\bullet$$

followed by

$$C_6H_5CHCl_2 + Cl\bullet \rightarrow C_6H_5CCl_2\bullet + HCl$$
$$C_6H_5CCl_2\bullet + Cl_2 \rightarrow C_6H_5CCl_3 + Cl\bullet$$

v) A fume cupboard protects the worker from excess chlorine, which is highly toxic, and from methylbenzene, chloromethylbenzenes and hydrogen chloride, all of which are harmful. In addition, all the organic chemicals are flammable.

EXERCISE 52

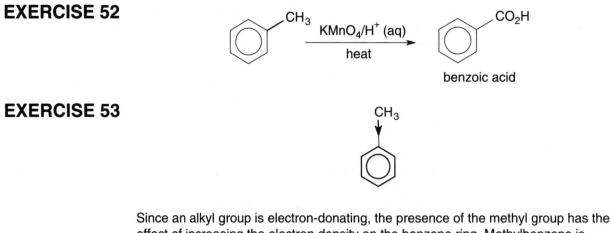

benzoic acid

EXERCISE 53

Since an alkyl group is electron-donating, the presence of the methyl group has the effect of increasing the electron density on the benzene ring. Methylbenzene is therefore more readily attacked than benzene by the electrophile NO_2^+.

EXERCISE 54

Chloro-2-methylbenzene

Chloro-4-methylbenzene

EXERCISE 55

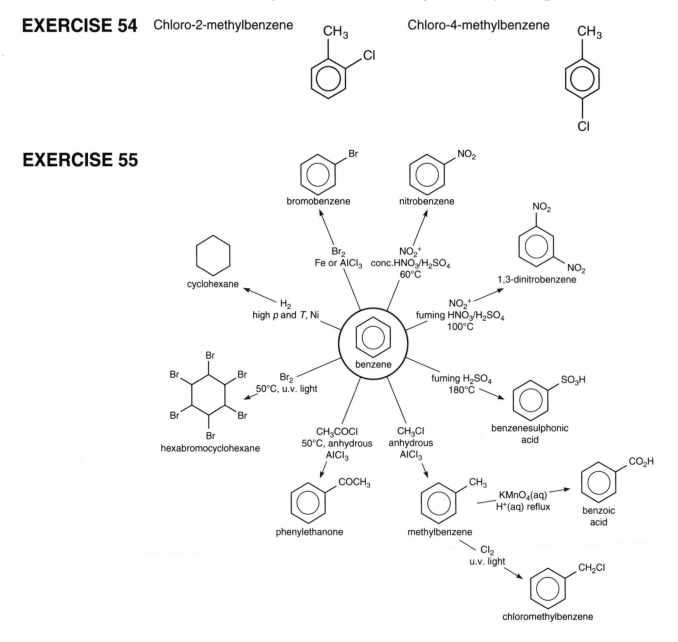

EXERCISE 56 **a** One theory states that petroleum was formed as a result of the decomposition of organisms once living in the sea. More recently, another theory has been put forward which suggests that petroleum originated through chemical reactions in the atmosphere at a very early stage in the earth's history.

b Magnetic surveys, gravity surveys and seismic surveys are used to locate oil deposits.

c Oil deposits, and associated natural gas, tend to rise through permeable layers of rock until trapped by an impermeable layer such as clay, shale or salt. The trap may be formed either by an upfold (anticline) caused by the buckling of the earth's crust, or by a fault.

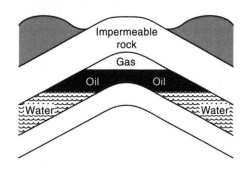

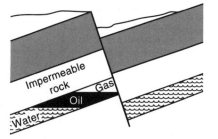

A fault trap

d In addition to cooling and lubricating the drill bit and bringing rock fragments to the surface, the mud also serves to counteract the upward pressure should a pocket of high-pressure gas or oil be struck. This often happened in the early days of drilling, causing a 'blow out'.

EXERCISE 57 **a** The Middle East.

b With the closing of the Suez Canal in 1956, tankers had to take the much longer route around the Cape of Good Hope.

c The longer journey round the Cape of Good Hope meant that it was more economical to use larger tankers.

d The oil industry had committed itself to using large tankers of around 200 000 tonnes, known as VLCCs (Very Large Crude Carriers), which were too large to take the shorter route through the Canal when it reopened.

(It is interesting to note that in the middle 1970s many giant ships were making their way to breakers' yards to be replaced by more sophisticated ships of around 100 000 tonnes. This was not only because of a drop in the demand for crude oil as the price had soared, but also because of the increased cost of running VLCCs on more expensive diesel fuel.) From the late 1980s, however, patterns changed again with VLCCs once again becoming the cheapest way of transporting oil. Shipyards now built ships up to 300 000 tonnes.

EXERCISE 58 **a** A = refinery gas C_1–C_4
                             B = gasoline (petrol) C_5–C_6
                             C = naphtha C_6–C_{10}
                             D = kerosene (paraffin oil) C_{10}–C_{16}
                             E = diesel oils (sometimes two fractions, light and heavy) C_{16}–C_{25}
                             F = residues   >C_{25}.

b In ascending order, each tray is cooler than the one below it, providing a temperature gradient in which separate vapours can condense. The bubble caps, which are fitted over the holes in the trays, deflect the rising vapours downwards so that they bubble through the liquids condensing on the trays. Maximum contact between ascending vapour and descending liquid ensures efficient fractionation.

c Lubricating oil, paraffin wax, fuel oil and bitumen.

d Refinery gas is used as fuel in the refinery and feedstock for the petrochemical industry.

Gasoline is used for petrol and solvents.

Naphtha is used as a feedstock for the chemical industry.

Kerosene (paraffin oil) is used as jet fuel and heating fuel.

Diesel oil is used as fuel for diesel engines.

Residues are further distilled under reduced pressure and the products used for lubricants, candles, road-surfacing and roofing.

e The primary use for oil in the early days was as a source of kerosene (paraffin) to burn in lamps and heaters. Until the advent of the internal combustion engine in the 1880s, the only products made from oil were kerosene, lubricants and some fuel oil. The remainder, including large quantities of gasoline (petrol), was burned off as unwanted waste. With the introduction of the motor car, the situation changed and gasoline became a major product. More recently, kerosene is again in demand as fuel for jet engines and heating systems.

EXERCISE 59 **a** i) Pre-ignition occurs when a fuel explodes under compression before a spark is passed. This with a subsequent explosion from the spark gives two shock waves, resulting in the characteristic 'knocking' noise of the engine.

b i) See Table 13 on page 137.

   ii) The octane scale goes from 0 to 100: the higher the number, the less tendency to pre-ignite in a car engine. Aromatic and highly branched chain aliphatic hydrocarbons cause least knocking.

c Catalytic cracking is the process by which alkanes are broken down into a mixture of smaller alkanes, alkenes and sometimes hydrogen.

In catalytic reforming, on the other hand, straight-chain alkanes are converted to branched-chain alkanes, cycloalkanes and arenes. The formation of rings also produces hydrogen.

d i) Cracking.

   ii) No single equation can represent the numerous individual reactions occurring during the cracking process. One example might be

$$C_{14}H_{30} \rightarrow C_{12}H_{26} + C_2H_4$$
$$\text{ethene}$$

e
$$C_{16}H_{34} + H_2 \rightarrow 2C_8H_{18}$$
$$\text{hexadecane} \qquad \text{octane}$$

Table 13	Hydrocarbon	Structure	Octane number
	Heptane		0
	Hexane		26
	2-Methylhexane		41
	Cyclohexane		77
	2,2-Dimethylpentane		89
	2,2,4-Trimethylpentane		100
	Benzene		108
	Methylbenzene		124

f i)

$$C_6H_{14} \rightarrow \text{⬡} + H_2$$

hexane   cyclohexane

(product will have a higher octane number)

ii)

$$\text{⬡} \rightarrow \text{⬡} + 3H_2$$

cyclohexane   benzene

(product will have a higher octane number)

g Hydrocracking as illustrated in part **e** above.

h Any equation which is balanced and results in a branched-chain isomer, e.g.

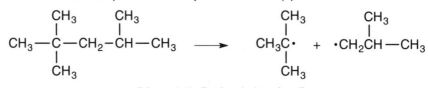

heptane

3,3-dimethylpentane

(Higher octane number than heptane)

The more branches to the carbon chain, the higher the octane number and hence the value of isomerisation.

i i) A free radical is a species with unpaired electron(s).

ii)

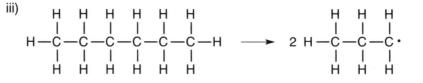

(Homolytic fission is involved)

iii)

$$H-\overset{\overset{\displaystyle H}{|}}{\underset{\underset{\displaystyle H}{|}}{C}}-\overset{\overset{\displaystyle H}{|}}{\underset{\underset{\displaystyle H}{|}}{C}}-\overset{\overset{\displaystyle H}{|}}{\underset{\underset{\displaystyle H}{|}}{C}}-\overset{\overset{\displaystyle H}{|}}{\underset{\underset{\displaystyle H}{|}}{C}}-\overset{\overset{\displaystyle H}{|}}{\underset{\underset{\displaystyle H}{|}}{C}}-\overset{\overset{\displaystyle H}{|}}{\underset{\underset{\displaystyle H}{|}}{C}}-H \longrightarrow 2\ H-\overset{\overset{\displaystyle H}{|}}{\underset{\underset{\displaystyle H}{|}}{C}}-\overset{\overset{\displaystyle H}{|}}{\underset{\underset{\displaystyle H}{|}}{C}}-\overset{\overset{\displaystyle H}{|}}{\underset{\underset{\displaystyle H}{|}}{C}}\cdot$$

iv) The products with the unbranched free radicals are the most reactive and cause the most knocking, i.e. the products from iii) above.

v)

$$(CH_3CH_2)_4Pb + 4\cdot \overset{\overset{\displaystyle CH_3}{|}}{CH}-CH_3 \longrightarrow 4CH_3-CH_2-\overset{\overset{\displaystyle CH_3}{|}}{CH}-CH_3 + Pb$$

The function of the tetraethyl lead(IV) is to help control the free radical chain reaction. When free radicals react with tetraethyl lead(IV) the chain is terminated because, as shown in the equation above, the final products are unreactive alkane molecules and lead atoms.

vi) Increase proportions of compounds which do not produce reactive free radicals, i.e. branched alkanes, cycloalkanes and arenes.

j The practice increases the environmental pollution by lead and is a hazard to health, particularly in children. Lead enters the body primarily by absorption of ingested lead and from inhaled air.

EXERCISE 60   **a** Eskdalemuir and Manchester represent rural and urban sites respectively. We should expect airborne concentrations to be higher in urban areas with heavier traffic and use of unleaded petrol.

b The fall in lead levels from 1985 follows from EU legislation which limited the amount of tetraethyl lead which could be added to petrol to 0.4 grams per litre in 1985 and 0.15 grams per litre in 1986. The increase in petrol consumption over the period has offset these falls to some extent.

c The dramatic increase in use of unleaded petrol shows up in Fig. 12 in March 1989 and through 1990, when the government launched a campaign to encourage motorists to switch to unleaded petrol.

d The catalysts would be poisoned and so ineffective if petrol containing lead was used.

e Since 1st January 1993, all new cars have had to be fitted with catalytic converters, so over the 10 years which follow this as old cars are scrapped and replaced by new, we should expect to see lead levels falling to a minimum when the majority of cars are running on unleaded petrol.

EXERCISE 61   **a** Fermentation. The starch in the grain is acted upon by enzymes in yeast which converts it into sugars and finally ethanol.

b Carbon dioxide.

c Advantage – renewable resource, **or** less drastic conditions are required. Disadvantage – produces weak ethanol solution which must then be distilled **or** slower reaction.

d Ethanol is used as a solvent and increasingly as a fuel/fuel additive.

EXERCISE 62   **a** i)

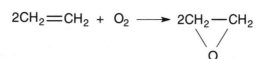

$$2CH_2{=}CH_2 + O_2 \longrightarrow 2CH_2{-}CH_2$$
                                         $$\backslash\,/$$
                                          $$O$$

epoxyethane

Air, Ag catalyst, 250°C

$$CH_2{-}CH_2 + H_2O \longrightarrow CH_2{-}CH_2$$
$$\backslash\,/\qquad\qquad\quad |\quad\ \ |$$
$$O\qquad\qquad\qquad OH\ \ OH$$

ethane-1,2-diol
(ethylene glycol)

H_2O, 200°C or H^+ (aq), 60°C

ii) $CH_2{=}CH_2 + Cl_2 \rightarrow CH_2ClCH_2Cl$
1,2-dichloroethane

$ZnCl_2$ catalyst, 50°C

$CH_2ClCH_2Cl \rightarrow CH_2{=}CHCl + HCl$
chloroethene
(vinyl chloride)

Pumice catalyst, 500°C, 3 atm

iii) $nCH_2{=}CH_2 \rightarrow (-CH_2{-}CH_2{-})_n$
polyethene

1. 'Low density polythene' Trace O_2, 200°C, 1500 atm
2. 'High density polythene', Ziegler catalyst, e.g. $TiCl_3/(C_2H_5)_3Al$, 50°C, 3 atm

iv)

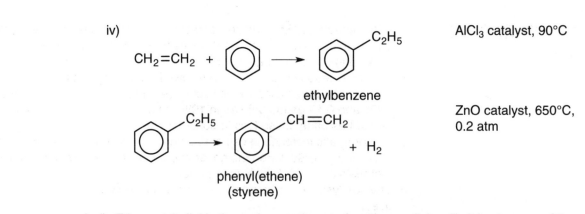

AlCl₃ catalyst, 90°C

ethylbenzene

ZnO catalyst, 650°C,
0.2 atm

phenyl(ethene)
(styrene)

b i) Ethane-1,2-diol is the main constituent of antifreeze ('glycol'). It is also one of the reactants needed to make terylene.

ii) Chloroethene (vinyl chloride) is the monomer from which polyvinyl chloride (PVC) is made.

iii) Polyethene is the well-known polymer used for making plastic bags, toys, etc.

iv) Phenylethene (styrene) is the monomer from which polyphenylethene (polystyrene) is made.

EXERCISE 63 a

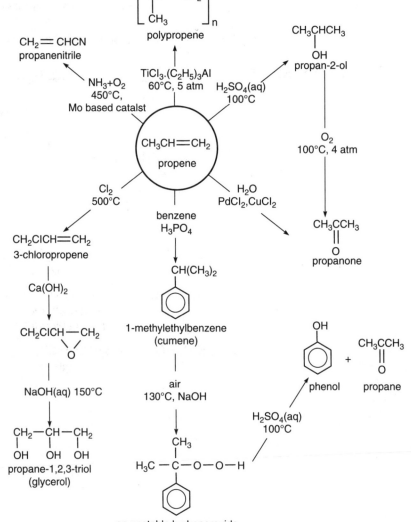

b Propenenitrile (acrylonitrile) is the monomer from which polypropenenitrile is made. The 'acrylic' fibre Orlon consists of polypropenenitrile, and Acrilan is a copolymer made from propenenitrile and ethenyl ethanoate, $CH_3COCH=CH_2$. Another copolymer, made from propenenitrile and buta-1,3-diene, $CH_2=CHCH=CH_2$, is known as nitrile rubber, which is used in chemical-resistant oil seals, gaskets and pipes.

Polypropene can replace polyethene in applications requiring greater strength or higher softening temperatures, e.g. kitchenware, hose-pipes.

Propan-2-ol is used as a solvent and in the manufacture of propanone and hydrogen peroxide.

Propanone (acetone) is used as a solvent and in the manufacture of Perspex.

Phenol is used in the manufacture of Bakelite, nylon, epoxy resins, weed-killers, antiseptics (e.g. Dettol), dyestuffs and insecticides.

Propane-1,2,3-triol (glycerol, glycerine) is used in the manufacture of glyptal resins and the explosive nitroglycerine.

EXERCISE 64

a The graph shows a decrease in the use of coal with a dramatic increase in the use of oil. Industry in Europe was built on coal throughout the last century and it was coal that fuelled the growth of industry after the Second World War. During the 1960s, however, coal lost a large part of the market as a result of the influx of cheap, easily handled oil from the Middle East. The drop in demand for coal for 1984 and the rise in demand of oil is a result of the coal-miners strike in that year.

b The discovery of large reserves of natural gas under the North Sea in 1965 made it economic for the Gas Board to supply natural gas rather than coal gas. The policy to change from coal- to gas-fired power stations in the early 1990s should result in a dramatic drop in the use of coal and arise in gas. This may continue into the year 2000, or at least until supplies of gas run out. To quote one official from Powergen – 'Coal has yet to have its day'.

c The demand for crude oil has dropped since the mid-1970s when the price soared. After the second oil price shock in 1979, oil demand fell steeply and the world entered an economic recession. In the second half of the 1980s the rate of reduction in oil production slowed and then reversed as demand increased.

EXERCISE 65

a In the Middle East.

b

$$\text{Estimated life of reserves} = \frac{\text{Reserves}}{\text{Production}} \text{ (R/P) ratio} = \frac{90}{0.925} = 97 \text{ years (approx.)}$$

Date of exhaustion $= 1992 + 97 = \mathbf{2089}$

Note that the discontinuity in the lower part of Fig. 16 obscures the fact that Middle East reserves are five times as great as Latin America's. This means that other reserves will run out much sooner. For instance, the R/P ratio for OECD Europe gives an estimated life of only 10 years.

EXERCISE 66

a and b

Fossil fuel	Estimated life of reserves/years	Percentage of total reserves
Oil	$\dfrac{137}{3.2} = 43$	$\dfrac{137}{774} \times 100 = 17.7\%$
Natural gas	$\dfrac{127}{1.8} = 71$	$\dfrac{127}{774} \times 100 = 16.4\%$
Coal	$\dfrac{510}{2.2} = 232$	$\dfrac{510}{774} \times 100 = 65.9\%$

c There is at present an imbalance between the resources and the rates of consumption of the different fossil fuels. The need to match consumption of fuels more closely to available reserves means that in the long term we can expect a significant increase in the use of coal as oil reserves become reduced. The conversion of power stations from coal to gas in the 1990s may in the short term see an increase in the consumption of gas but it too will eventually have to give way to coal or some other energy source.

d The estimated life of a fossil fuel resource is based on two assumptions which are quite likely to prove false.

1. Rate of consumption remains constant.
2. No new reserves are discovered.

(Some people take the view that any increase in consumption will be outweighed, or at least balanced, by new discoveries, as has happened in the past; others regard this view as overoptimistic.)

EXERCISE 67
Table 16

Pollutant	Sulphur dioxide	Hydrocarbons	Carbon monoxide	Ozone	Nitrogen oxides
Source	Combustion of sulphur-containing fossil fuels	Unburnt hydrocarbons from exhaust emissions, emissions during refuelling and distribution of fuels	Incomplete combustion of fuel	In the lower atmosphere formed by a photochemical reaction involving nitrogen oxides, oxygen and sunlight	Motor vehicles are the main source (45%). Power stations emit a further 35%
Health effects	Breathing problems, e.g. bronchitis. Asthmatics are particularly badly affected. Most serious when it combines with the moisture in the lungs to form sulphuric acid	Aromatics can be carcinogens. Benzene has been linked with leukaemia	Deprives the body of oxygen by reacting with haemoglobin. Causes drowsiness and headaches. Fatal at high concentrations	Beneficial in the upper atmosphere but harmful at ground level. High concentrations can damage lung tissue and the immune system. Aggravates asthma and bronchitis	Irritates lung tissue, increased risk of bronchitis and pneumonia
Environmental effects	The main constituent of acid rain, which damages aquatic life and increases concentrations of heavy metals in acidified water. Corrosion of buildings	Along with ozone, contributes to the formation of photochemical smog	Oxidises to carbon dioxide, the greenhouse gas	Major component of 'photochemical smog'; damages plastics, rubber, paints and crops by reducing yields	Responsible for about one third of the acidity of rainfall

EXERCISE 68   **a** i) Industrial Revolution (steam engines ran on coal).
ii) Recession (or 'slump').
iii) Post-war boom.
iv) Increased use of gas after its discovery in the North Sea.
b $OH^• + SO_2 + O_2 = HO_2^• + SO_3$. $SO_3 + H_2O = H_2SO_4$

EXERCISE 69   **a** Power stations.
b Coal and fuel oil.
c $[(4897 - 3565)/4897] \times 100 = $ **27.2%**.

EXERCISE 70   **a** Exercise 69**c** showed a 27.2% drop in 11 years.
Therefore in 18 years the drop would be $27.2 \times (18/11) = $ **45%**.
So 1998 target of 40% reduction would be met.
However, in 23 years the drop would be $27.2 \times (23/11) = $ **57%**.
So 2003 target of 60% would **not** be met.

Option	Advantages	Disadvantages
Increased use of nuclear power	Bring down SO_2 and CO_2 levels	Problems of safely disposing of radioactive waste and accidents, e.g. Chernobyl disaster
Change from coal- to gas-fired power station*	Gas does not contain sulphur therefore it would bring down SO_2 levels. Electrical industry claims it will make electricity cheaper	Job losses if coal pits close. More gas imports will be needed when North Sea gas runs out
Increase the energy from renewable sources	The use of renewables such as wind, solar and wave power not only conserves remaining stocks of fossil fuels but would bring down air pollutant levels. The burning of municipal rubbish and sewage gas exploits waste which has to be disposed of anyway and solves some unsightly messes as well. Hydro-electricity, the oldest form of large-scale renewable energy, could be developed further	Many of these alternative sources of energy are still in the experimental stage. People would have to get used to seeing hills covered in windmills or an estuary equipped with a tidal-power barrage which might attract fewer birds. Care must be taken to ensure large dams for hydro-electricity are built with respect for local environment
Increased energy efficiency (e.g. insulating the home and reducing the number of vehicles on the road. Limiting cities to public transport has been proposed)	Uses less of our valuable non-renewable fossil fuels and conserves them as chemical feedstock for future generations	There is no one big solution but hundreds of little ones. To achieve these requires money, effort and political will to educate people in energy efficiency. (This should be considered an advantage)
Install flue-gas desulphur-isation plants (FGDs)	These get rid of up to 90% of sulphur dioxide emissions	Requires a lot of limestone. High installation cost of FGD

*The government's policy at the time of writing is to phase out coal-fired power stations and replace them with gas.

EXERCISE 71

a As the resulting CO_2 escapes there will be a lot of effervescence.

b i) The amount of $CaCO_3$ is given by substituting into the expression

$$n = \frac{m}{M} = \frac{1 \times 10^{10}\ g}{100\ g\ mol^{-1}}$$

$$= 1 \times 10^8\ mol$$

Since 1 mol $CaCO_3$ reacts with 1 mol SO_2, the mass of SO_2 is given by substituting into the expression

$m = nM$

$= 1 \times 10^8\ mol \times 64\ g\ mol^{-1} = 64 \times 10^8\ g$

= 6400 tonnes.

ii) The mass of $CaSO_4 \cdot 2H_2O$ is given by substituting into the expression

$m = nM$

$= 1 \times 10^8\ mol \times 172\ g\ mol^{-1}$

$= 172 \times 10^8\ g =$ **17 200 tonnes**.

iii) The amount of coal (C) is given by substituting into the expression

$$n = \frac{m}{M} = \frac{1.2 \times 10^{11}\ g}{12\ g\ mol^{-1}} = 1 \times 10^{10}\ mol$$

The mass of CO_2 is given by substituting into

$m = nM = 1 \times 10^{10}\ mol \times 44\ g\ mol^{-1}$

$= 4.4 \times 10^{11}\ g =$ **4.4 $\times 10^5$ tonnes**.

iv) 1×10^8 mol $CaCO_3$ will produce 1×10^8 mol CO_2.

The mass of CO_2 is given by substituting into the expression

$m = nM = 1 \times 10^8\ mol \times 44\ g\ mol^{-1}$

= 44 $\times 10^8$ g = 4.4 $\times 10^3$ tonnes.

c Manufacture of plaster of Paris and plasterboard. Any surplus is being taken by 'British Gypsum' to fill in old Gypsum mines!

d No, an addition of 1% which is trivial.

EXERCISE 72

a **List of key points**: these may occur in any order, and it is not necessary for them to be expressed in these words provided that the sense of each point is conveyed:

1. Formation of ozone in (upper) atmosphere (equations preferred).
2. Constant removal of ozone (equations preferred).
3. Resulting equilibrium situation.
4. Absorption of harmful ultraviolet radiation in upper atmosphere.
5. Absorption of infrared in lower atmosphere, with warming effect.
6. Ability of ozone to react with free radicals.
7. Ozone removed by chlorine atoms from breakdown of CFCs in upper atmosphere (equations preferred).
8. Resulting decrease in ozone concentration.
9. Formation of ozone caused by NO_2 from burning fossil fuels (equations preferred).
10. Ozone reacts with unburnt hydrocarbons to produce photochemical smog.

(Max. 10 marks.)

To gain the mark for a key point the wording used must make clear the essential chemistry of the point.

Style use of English scores 0–2 marks (Max. 2 marks)

Word penalty up to 153 words   no penalty

154–160   −1

161–165   −2

166–170   −3

Rate of −1 for every 5 words in excess, up to a maximum of −10. (Total: 12 marks)

Here are a few comments from the examiner who marked some of these answers the year this question was set.

'A majority of candidates picked out more than half the key points. However a significant minority of candidates produced summaries which **excluded** all the relevant chemistry instead of including it. The usual result in these cases is a piece of 'popular journalism' containing little to credit! . . . On the other hand, a few candidates insisted on the inclusion of **all** the chemistry in the passage, whether relevant to the role of ozone in the atmosphere or not; there was no specific penalty for doing so, but penalties were given for missing other points or exceeding the maximum word total. One common misunderstanding of the chemistry given in the passage concerned the reactions in the lower atmosphere, where a significant proportion of candidates seemed unable to distinguish the role of nitrogen oxides in the upper atmosphere from their role in the lower atmosphere, hence confusing the mechanisms for removal of ozone with those for its formation. Candidates should be advised to make effective use of relevant equations in writing their summaries; incorporating equations into the text, rather than presenting them separately.'

b i) Ozone affects the eyes and lungs and contributes to photochemical smog.

ii) An equilibrium situation arises from the two processes:

To form ozone $O_2 \rightarrow 2 \cdot O \cdot$ followed by $O_2 + \cdot O \cdot \rightarrow O_3$

To remove ozone $O_3 + \cdot O \cdot \rightarrow 2O_2$ and $NO + O_3 \rightarrow NO_2 + O_2$

iii) The photochemical reactions which give rise to ozone require ultraviolet radiation which is more intensive in summer ozone episodes when there are long hours of bright sunlight, temperatures above $20°C$ and light winds. Once formed, ozone can persist for several days and can be transported long distances.

iv) NO_2 is dissociated by ultraviolet radiation

$$NO_2 \overset{hv}{\rightarrow} NO + \cdot O \cdot$$

The oxygen free radical then reacts with O_2 to produce ozone

$$O_2 + \cdot O \cdot \rightarrow O_3$$

v) Hydrocarbons.

vi) Emissions from car exhausts.

c i) Ozone absorbs ultraviolet light before it can reach the earth. Less ozone in the upper atmosphere (stratosphere) means the earth receives more harmful ultraviolet rays which can cause sunburn or, more seriously, can lead to skin cancer.

ii) Chlorofluorocarbons (CFCs) which originate from aerosols, refrigerators and foams.

iii)
$$Cl \cdot + O_3 = ClO + O_2 \tag{1}$$

$$ClO + \cdot O \cdot = Cl \cdot + O_2 \tag{2}$$

The free radical product of one reaction is a reagent for the other and vice versa, e.g. the product for reaction (2) above ($Cl\cdot$) is a reagent for reaction (1).

This goes on until something destroys the free radical. In this way one $Cl\cdot$ free radical can destroy thousands of ozone molecules.

iv)
$$O_3 + \cdot O \cdot = 2O_2$$

v) Chlorine is a catalyst.

vi) Stop using CFCs and find suitable alternatives. (You look at possible alternatives in the next chapter dealing with halogenoalkanes.)

EXERCISE 73

a This provides an increased surface area over which gases can interact.

b Platinum, palladium and rhodium. These are transition metals from the d-block elements.

c CO_2 – from combustion of fuel,
CO – from incomplete combustion of fuel,
HCs – from unburnt fuel,
NO_2 – from the combination of nitrogen and oxygen from the air at high temperatures in the engine cylinders.

d i) $C_6H_{14} + 9\frac{1}{2}O_2 \xrightarrow{Pt} 6CO_2 + 7H_2O$

   ii) $CO + \frac{1}{2}O_2 \xrightarrow{Pt} CO_2$

e $4CO + 2NO_2 \xrightarrow{Rd} 4CO_2 + N_2$

EXERCISE 74

a $CO_2 \approx 50$ mph,
CO ≈ 50 mph,
HCs ≈ 60 mph,
$NO_x \approx 30$ mph.

b i) Cars and buses could have speed limits of about 55 mph with governors.
   ii) Governors not only increase safety and reduce pollution but they also reduce fuel consumption. These advantages offset increased journey times.

EXERCISE 75

a Incomplete combustion of fuel brought about by a blocked flue or chimney or insufficient air inlet.

b You can't see or smell carbon monoxide. The early symptoms include tiredness, drowsiness and headache.

c Carbon monoxide combines irreversibly with the haemoglobin in the blood, preventing it from carrying oxygen. Your body is therefore starved of oxygen.

d Make sure the flue is unblocked, and if a gas appliance is used, make sure it is serviced regularly. **Never** use a gas appliance if you think it is not working properly. Signs to look out for include yellow or orange flames, soot or stains around the appliance and pilot lights which frequently blow out. **Never** use a gas oven to heat a room. **Always** ventilate a room if water is heated by an old open flued gas water heater.

EXERCISE 76

a 2-Chlorobutane,
b 2-bromo-2-methylpropane,
c iodoethane,
d 1,4-dichlorobenzene,
e 1-chloro-3-methylbenzene,
f (chloromethyl)benzene.

Note how the brackets in **f** show that it is the methyl group, not the benzene ring, which is chloro-substituted.

EXERCISE 77

a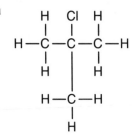

b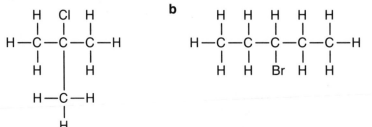

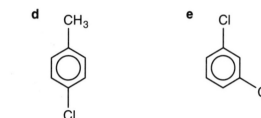

EXERCISE 78   **b** and **e** are primary halogenoalkanes.
a is a secondary halogenoalkane.
c and **d** are tertiary halogenoalkanes.

EXERCISE 79   The trend in bond energy values suggests that we can list the halogen compounds
with the most reactive first in the order:

$$C_4H_9I > C_4H_9Br > C_4H_9Cl > C_6H_5Cl$$

EXPERIMENT 3

Results Table 4

Reaction	Time for precipitate to appear	Observations
A 1-Chlorobutane	8 minutes	Faint still after 30 minutes
B 1-Bromobutane	2 minutes	Denser after 5 minutes. Settling beginning after 30 minutes
C 1-Iodobutane	30 seconds	Heavy yellow after 1 minute. Settled after 30 minutes
D Chlorobenzene		No precipitate even after 1 hour

Questions   1. 1-Iodobutane, 1-bromobutane, 1-chlorobutane, chlorobenzene.
2. Yes, the list predicting potential reactivity coincides with the order of speed of hydrolysis.

3. $CH_3CH_2CH_2CH_2X + H_2O \rightarrow CH_3CH_2CH_2CH_2OH + H^+ (aq) + X^- (aq)$
butan-1-ol   (X = Cl, Br or I)

EXERCISE 80   **a** Iodoalkanes are often used because they are more reactive than other halogenoalkanes due to the weak C—I bond. (However, iodo-compounds are rarely used
industrially because they are more expensive than the other halogen compounds.)
b The trend in bond energy values in Table 20 suggests that the C—F bond is
stronger than the C–halogen bond in other halogeno-alkanes, and probably
stronger than the C—Cl bond in chlorobenzene. Even at cooking temperatures,
there is insufficient energy to break the C—F bond.
(PTFE is so stable that it does not even react with sodium below 400°C.)

EXERCISE 81   The interaction of the unbonded (non-bonded) electrons on the chlorine atom with the
delocalised ring system, as shown in Fig. 27, has the effect of strengthening the C—Cl
bond. This accounts for the fact that chlorobenzene cannot be hydrolysed in test-tube
conditions. (It can, however, be hydrolysed in more drastic conditions, using a high
temperature and a catalyst, as shown below.)

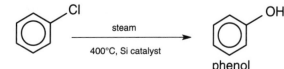

EXERCISE 82   **a** Put 2 cm^3 of ethanol in each of two test-tubes. Add 3 drops of chlorobenzene to one test-tube and 3 drops of (chloromethyl)benzene to the other. Add 1 cm^3 of aqueous silver nitrate to each and heat to 60°C. A white precipitate of AgCl forms slowly in the tube containing (chloromethyl)benzene, due to the hydrolysis of the (chloromethyl)benzene to phenyl methanol.

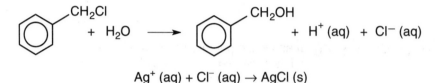

$$Ag^+ (aq) + Cl^- (aq) \rightarrow AgCl (s)$$

There is no precipitate in the tube containing chlorobenzene.
(Hydrolysis is more rapid using OH$^-$ (aq), as you see in the next section.)

b The procedure is the same as for part **a**. A yellow precipitate of AgI forms very rapidly from the iodopropane; a white precipitate of AgCl forms more slowly from the chloropropane. Hydrolysis occurs, followed by precipitation.

$$C_3H_7X + H_2O \rightarrow C_3H_7OH + H^+ (aq) + X^- (aq)$$

$$Ag^+ (aq) + X^- (aq) \rightarrow AgX (s)$$

EXERCISE 83   **a** In a nucleophilic substitution, a lone pair of electrons on a nucleophile, such as OH$^-$, H$_2$O or NH$_3$, is attracted to a carbon atom with a partial positive charge. The nucleophile is then substituted for the atom or group attached to the carbon atom.

b The polarisation of the carbon–halogen bond gives the carbon atom a partial positive charge which makes it susceptible to attack by a nucleophile. Also, the halogen atom can form a stable leaving ion.

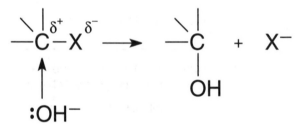

EXERCISE 84   **a** i) $C_4H_9Br + OH^- \rightarrow C_4H_9OH + Br^-$ (Heat with aqueous
                           butan-1-ol   NaOH.)

   ii) $C_4H_9Br + CN^- \rightarrow C_4H_9CN + Br^-$ (Reflux with KCN
                          pentanenitrile   solution in ethanol.)

   This reaction is useful in synthesis reactions where you want to increase the length of a carbon chain.
   (A reminder: refluxing is the process of boiling volatile reactants in a flask connected to a condenser which is fitted vertically so that condensed liquid runs back into the flask. In this way, the liquid mixture can be maintained at a fairly high temperature for a long period of time without loss by evaporation.)

   iii) $C_4H_9Br + CH_3CO_2^-Ag^+ \rightarrow CH_3CO_2C_4H_9 + AgBr$ (Heat in ethanol
                                    1-butyl ethanoate   solution.)

   iv) $C_4H_9Br + C_2H_5O^- \rightarrow C_2H_5OC_4H_9 + Br^-$ (Reflux with
                               1-ethoxybutane   C$_2$H$_5$ONa in
                                                                                          ethanol.)

   v) $C_4H_9Br + H_2O \rightarrow C_4H_9OH + H^+ + Br^-$ (Heat. Slow –
                           butan-1-ol   better to use OH$^-$.)

vi) $\qquad$ $C_4H_9Br + 2NH_3 \rightarrow C_4H_9NH_2 + NH_4Br$ (Heat with
$\qquad\qquad\qquad\qquad\qquad$ butylamine $\qquad\qquad$ excess NH_3 in
$\qquad\qquad\qquad\qquad\qquad\qquad\qquad\qquad\qquad\qquad\qquad$ ethanol in a
$\qquad\qquad\qquad\qquad\qquad\qquad\qquad\qquad\qquad\qquad\qquad$ sealed tube.)

If the ammonia is not in excess, further substitution can occur to give $(C_4H_9)_2NH$, $(C_4H_9)_3N$ and $(C_4H_9)_4N^+Br^-$.

b The hydroxide ion, OH^-, is a stronger nucleophile than water and substitution occurs more readily.

EXERCISE 85 **a**

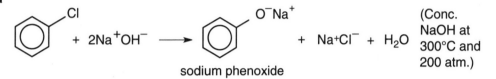

(Conc. NaOH at 300°C and 200 atm.)

Phenol can be obtained from sodium phenoxide by treating with an acid:

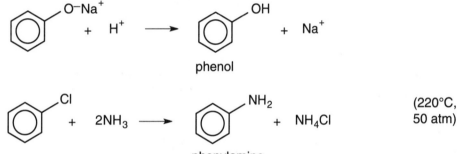

b

Cl + $2NH_3$ ⟶ NH₂ + NH_4Cl (220°C, 50 atm)

phenylamine

EXERCISE 86 The delocalisation system associated with the double bond is extended to include a non-bonding p-orbital on the chlorine. The additional electron density between the C and Cl atoms strengthens the bond and makes the molecule less susceptible to substitution.

EXERCISE 87

$:OH^-$ + (1-bromopropane) ⟶ [activated complex] ⟶ (propan-1-ol) + Br^-

1-bromopropane $\qquad$ activated complex $\qquad$ propan-1-ol

EXERCISE 88 **a** The active species is the ethoxide ion, $C_2H_5O^-$, produced from the reaction between potassium hydroxide and the ethanol in which it is dissolved.

$$C_2H_5OH + KOH \rightarrow C_2H_5O^-K^+ + H_2O$$
$$\text{potassium}$$
$$\text{ethoxide}$$

b $\qquad$ $CH_3CHICH_3 + C_2H_5O^- \rightarrow CH_3CH{=}CH_2 + C_2H_5OH + I^-$
$\qquad\qquad\qquad\qquad\qquad\qquad\qquad$ propene $\qquad\qquad$ ethanol

EXERCISE 89 Table 21 Methods of preparing halogen compounds

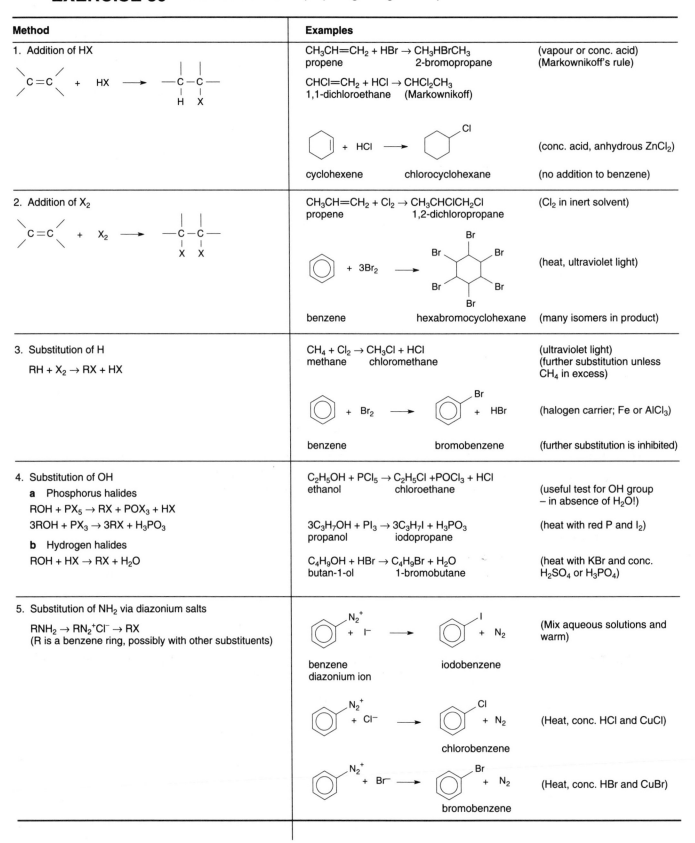

Method	Examples	
1. Addition of HX	$CH_3CH{=}CH_2 + HBr \rightarrow CH_3HBrCH_3$ propene 2-bromopropane	(vapour or conc. acid) (Markownikoff's rule)
	$CHCl{=}CH_2 + HCl \rightarrow CHCl_2CH_3$ 1,1-dichloroethane (Markownikoff)	
	cyclohexene + HCl $\longrightarrow$ chlorocyclohexane	(conc. acid, anhydrous $ZnCl_2$) (no addition to benzene)
2. Addition of X_2	$CH_3CH{=}CH_2 + Cl_2 \rightarrow CH_3CHClCH_2Cl$ propene 1,2-dichloropropane	(Cl_2 in inert solvent)
	benzene + $3Br_2$ $\longrightarrow$ hexabromocyclohexane	(heat, ultraviolet light) (many isomers in product)
3. Substitution of H $RH + X_2 \rightarrow RX + HX$	$CH_4 + Cl_2 \rightarrow CH_3Cl + HCl$ methane chloromethane	(ultraviolet light) (further substitution unless CH_4 in excess)
	benzene + Br_2 $\longrightarrow$ bromobenzene + HBr	(halogen carrier; Fe or $AlCl_3$) (further substitution is inhibited)
4. Substitution of OH **a** Phosphorus halides $ROH + PX_5 \rightarrow RX + POX_3 + HX$ $3ROH + PX_3 \rightarrow 3RX + H_3PO_3$ **b** Hydrogen halides $ROH + HX \rightarrow RX + H_2O$	$C_2H_5OH + PCl_5 \rightarrow C_2H_5Cl + POCl_3 + HCl$ ethanol chloroethane $3C_3H_7OH + PI_3 \rightarrow 3C_3H_7I + H_3PO_3$ propanol iodopropane $C_4H_9OH + HBr \rightarrow C_4H_9Br + H_2O$ butan-1-ol 1-bromobutane	(useful test for OH group – in absence of H_2O!) (heat with red P and I_2) (heat with KBr and conc. H_2SO_4 or H_3PO_4)
5. Substitution of NH_2 via diazonium salts $RNH_2 \rightarrow RN_2^+Cl^- \rightarrow RX$ (R is a benzene ring, possibly with other substituents)	benzene diazonium ion + I^- $\longrightarrow$ iodobenzene + N_2	(Mix aqueous solutions and warm)
	+ Cl^- $\longrightarrow$ chlorobenzene + N_2	(Heat, conc. HCl and CuCl)
	+ Br^- $\longrightarrow$ bromobenzene + N_2	(Heat, conc. HBr and CuBr)

EXERCISE 90 The equation tells us that 1 mol of ethanol produces 1 mol of iodoethane. Using the expression:

$$\text{Density} = \frac{\text{Mass}}{\text{Volume}}$$

mass of ethanol $= 0.79 \text{ g cm}^{-3} \times 5.0 \text{ cm}^3 = 3.95 \text{ g}$.

Using $n = \dfrac{m}{M}$, amount of ethanol $= \dfrac{3.95 \text{ g}}{46 \text{ g mol}^{-1}} = 0.086 \text{ mol}$

So, we should expect to produce 0.086 mol of iodoethane.

Maximum mass of iodoethane from amount using $m = nM$ gives
$m = 0.086 \text{ mol} \times 156 \text{ g mol}^{-1} = 13.4 \text{ g}$.
Substitution into the expression

$$\% \text{ yield} = \frac{\text{actual mass of product}}{\text{maximum mass of product}} \times 100 = \frac{5.1 \text{ g}}{13.4 \text{ g}} \times 100 = \mathbf{38\%}$$

EXPERIMENT 4
Specimen results
Results Table 5

Mass of measuring cylinder + 2-methylpropan-2-ol	50.8 g
Mass of measuring cylinder after emptying	43.7 g
Mass of 2-methylpropan-2-ol	7.1 g
Mass of collecting flask	32.2 g
Mass of collecting flask + 2-chloro-2-methylpropane	37.7 g
Mass of 2-chloro-2-methylpropane	5.5 g

Questions 1.

$$\text{Amount of (CH}_3)_3\text{COH used} = \frac{7.1 \text{ g}}{74 \text{ g mol}^{-1}} = 0.096 \text{ mol}$$

The equation shows 1 mol of $(CH_3)_3CCl$ formed from 1 mol of $(CH_3)_3COH$
∴ the maximum possible amount of $(CH_3)_3CCl = 0.096$ mol
and the maximum mass $= 0.096 \text{ mol} \times 92.5 \text{ g mol}^{-1} = \mathbf{8.9 \text{ g}}$

2.
$$\% \text{ yield} = \frac{\text{actual mass of product}}{\text{maximum mass of product}} \times 100 = \frac{5.5 \text{ g}}{8.9 \text{ g}} \times 100 = \mathbf{62\%}$$

3. A stronger alkali would tend to hydrolyse the halogeno-compound back to the alcohol.

EXERCISE 91 Amount of 2-chloro-2-methylpropane produced using

$$n = \frac{m}{M} = \frac{5.5 \text{ g}}{92.5 \text{ g mol}^{-1}} = 0.059 \text{ mol}$$

From the equation, 1 mol of 2-chloro-2-methylpropane is produced from 1 mol of 2-methylpropan-2-ol. For a 100% yield the amount of 2-methylpropan-1-ol required would also be 0.059 mol.

For a 62% yield we should need more reactant to compensate for the loss of the product, so

$$\text{the amount of 2-methylpropan-1-ol} = \frac{100}{62} \times 0.059 \text{ mol} = 0.095 \text{ mol}$$

Converting this to mass gives $m = 0.095 \text{ mol} \times 74 \text{ g mol}^{-1} = 7.0 \text{ g}$

Converting this to volume using

$$\text{Volume} = \frac{7.0 \text{ g}}{0.79 \text{ g cm}^{-3}} = \textbf{9.0 cm}^3 \textbf{ of 2-methylpropan-1-ol}$$

We should also expect to use 0.095 mol HCl. Converting this to mass gives $m = 0.095$ mol $\times 36.5$ g mol^{-1} = 3.5 g.

Since the hydrochloric acid is 32% acid, in order to obtain 3.5 g of hydrochloric acid we shall need to use (100/32) $\times$ 3.5 g = 10.9 g of the given acid solution. Convert this mass to volume from the given density, so

$$\text{Volume} \approx \frac{10.9 \text{ g}}{1.16 \text{ g cm}^{-3}} = \textbf{9.4 cm}^3 \textbf{ of hydrochloric acid}$$

This volume of acid represents the minimum volume required. Often more than this is used to ensure all of the alcohol reacts.

EXERCISE 92
Figure 30
Summary of preparations and properties of 1-bromopropane.

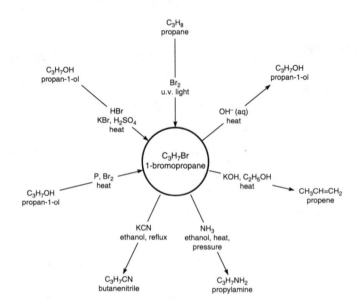

Figure 31
Summary of preparations and properties of bromobenzene.

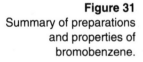

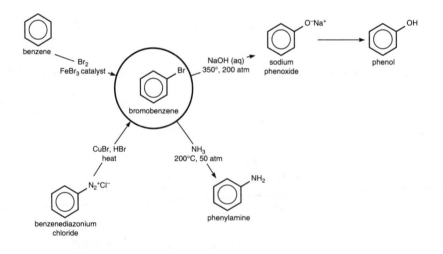

EXERCISE 93   a

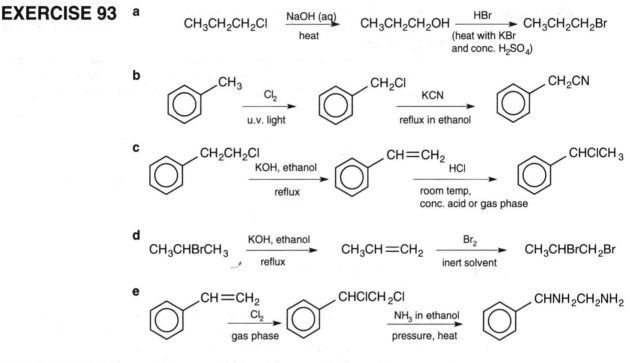

CH₃CH₂CH₂Cl $\xrightarrow[\text{heat}]{\text{NaOH (aq)}}$ CH₃CH₂CH₂OH $\xrightarrow[\substack{\text{(heat with KBr}\\\text{and conc. H}_2\text{SO}_4)}]{\text{HBr}}$ CH₃CH₂CH₂Br

EXERCISE 94   a Gammexane, which is one of the geometrical isomers of 1,2,3,4,5,6-hexachlorocyclohexane, C₆H₆Cl₆, is a powerful insecticide.

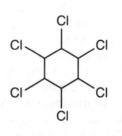

b DDT was at first thought to be harmless to birds and animals (including man) because the small amounts likely to be absorbed directly as a result of spraying procedures cause no toxic effects. However, because DDT is very stable and fat-soluble, it persists for a long time in food chains and toxic levels can be built up over a period in animals at the end of these food chains.

c Very low reactivity and toxicity (largely due to the strong C—F bonds), together with low boiling points, are the chief properties which make CFCs useful.

d CFCs are inert in the lower atmosphere but when they reach the stratosphere they undergo photochemical decomposition to form chlorine radicals, simultaneously catalysing the destruction of ozone.

e Tetrachloroethene, CCl₂CCl₂ (tradename Perk) is now the most widely used solvent but it is toxic and possibly carcinogenic. Emissions can be reduced with recovery equipment, which is already widely used, but needs to be maintained and operated properly. This has a lower ozone depletion potential than carbon tetrachloride or 1,1,1-trichloroethane. Alternatives are being sought which contain **no chlorine**, are **non-toxic** and have **low flammability**. To quote Friends of the Earth: 'The best long term solution will be to move towards water-washable clothes.'

f Fluothane, CHClBrCF₃, is used as an anaesthetic.

EXERCISE 95
  a Compound C is 1,1-dichloro-2,2,2-trifluoroethane.

  b Compound B can be obtained from the natural source, crude oil. The others have to be synthesised.

  c A cleaning solvent must be a liquid at room temperature which of course B is not. (Even though some manufacturers are now using compounds like B as propellants in aerosol cans, the fact that they are flammable makes them less safe.)

  d i)

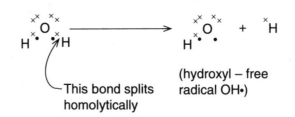

    More usually written: $H_2O \rightarrow OH\bullet + H\bullet$

  ii) Equation 7.1 $H\bullet$

    Equation 7.2 $CF_3CCl_2\bullet$

  iii) In a propagation step (chain reaction) the free radical product of one reaction is a reagent for the other and vice versa. (In this case the $OH^\bullet$ radical.) This goes on until something destroys the free radical.

  e HFAs have no chlorine so they won't have an effect on the ozone layer, i.e. zero ODP value. HCFCs have chlorine in them but also have a carbon–hydrogen bond. This means, as you have seen in your answer to part **d**, that it will be readily broken down (photolysed) at ground level and so have less chance of getting to the stratosphere. We should not expect a zero ODP but certainly lower than for CFCs.

  f Points to include.

  Advantages of C:

  ■ Low ODP value results from the presence of the carbon–hydrogen bond. This means they break down at ground level so there is less chance of getting into the stratosphere to release chlorine free radicals.

  ■ Non-flammable so can be used safely.

  ■ Liquid at room temperature so can be used as a cleaning solvent.

  Disadvantages of C:

  ■ Does still contain chlorine so there is some effect on the ozone layer.

  ■ Cost is treble that of CFCs so the products are more expensive.